DMU 0363744 01 0

KT-487-811

How To Keep Your Horse Healthy

Withdrawn

Colin Vogel
B.Vet.Med., MRCVS

Lincolnshire College of Agriculture and Horticulture, ~~Riseholme~~ CAYTHORPE

INSTRUCTIONS TO BORROWERS

Please replace on the correct shelf any books you take down for use in the library room.

Books taken out

Enter your name and date on the card, and place the card in the box provided.
You may keep the book for a fortnight, after which it should be returned.

Return of borrowed books

These should be returned to the Enquiry Office or placed in the slot in the library and NOT replaced on the shelves.

BSP PROFESSIONAL BOOKS
OXFORD LONDON EDINBURGH
BOSTON MELBOURNE

Copyright © C. J. Vogel 1989

All rights reserved. No part of this publication may be reproduced, stored in a retrieval system, or transmitted, in any form or by any means, electronic, mechanical, photocopying, recording or otherwise without the prior permission of the copyright owner.

First published 1989

British Library
Cataloguing in Publication Data

Vogel, C.J. (Colin J.)
How to keep your horse healthy.
1. Livestock. Horses. Preventive veterinary medicine
I. Title
636.1'08944

ISBN 0–632–02588–3
ISBN 0–632–02056–3 Pbk

BSP Professional Books
A division of Blackwell Scientific Publications Ltd
Editorial Offices:
Osney Mead, Oxford OX2 0EL
(Orders: Tel. 0865 240201)
8 John Street, London WC1N 2ES
23 Ainslie Place, Edinburgh EH3 6AJ
3 Cambridge Center, Suite 208, Cambridge, MA 02142, USA
107 Barry Street, Carlton, Victoria 3053, Australia

Typeset by DP Photosetting, Aylesbury, Bucks
Printed and bound in Great Britain by Mackays of Chatham PLC, Chatham, Kent

Contents

1 Introduction

Preventing equine disease

How to Keep Your Horse Healthy is not written as a reference book. Rather it is a practical guide providing information and advice which you, the horse owner, will want to use continually out in the stable. It is not an equine veterinary dictionary. Nor is it in any way a guide to the diseases of the horse. You will find plenty of diseases and conditions described in the course of the text, some of them in considerable detail, but this is done in order to help you to avoid them rather than merely to educate you. So preventive medicine is what this book is all about. If you can avoid some of the problems discussed in later chapters, you will get more fun out of your horse because your horse will spend less time on the sidelines unable to compete.

The advantages of preventive medicine

Preventive medicine is extremely cost effective. Everyone knows the old adage 'a stitch in time saves nine'. Relatively small amounts of expenditure on vaccination, for instance, can save you large veterinary bills for treating the disease itself. You will notice that I said 'relatively small amounts'. There are some people who consider that a veterinary surgeon should not charge for advice about preventive medicine 'because he hasn't had to cure anything'. One could say that it ought to be the other way round, and that horse owners should be prepared to pay more for advice and drugs which are effective enough to prevent disease. It is an unfortunate fact that modern drugs and vaccines cost considerable amounts of money. The better and more effective we want our vaccines to be, the safer we want them to be, and the more sophisticated we want them to be, the more we will have to pay for them.

There is one further point on the economics of preventive medicine. This concerns the wear and tear on the horse itself. By and large, a disease always takes something out of the horse; it always places some extra stress on the body systems. If we think of a motor car, it might travel 20 000 miles before it needs new brake pads. If, however, it is being driven in such a way that it is continually being braked sharply at every bend and junction, then it might need new brake pads after only 15 000 miles. The horse's respiratory system, for example, is more likely to develop chronic problems if the horse suffers several attacks of acute respiratory disease such as equine influenza. The great difference between a car and a horse (besides the wheels) is that you can replace a worn-out part on a car, but you cannot for example, give a horse a new leg or a new pair of lungs. So a healthy horse will serve you longer, and if you should want to sell it for any reason, it will keep its value better.

Buying a healthy horse

The best standards of horse care in the world, however, cannot hope to reverse chronic disease processes which have existed for months or even years. Preventive medicine starts before you even buy the horse. You must try to ensure that the horse you are buying is as sound as possible. Soundness in this connection with horses means that the horse is not suffering from any condition which does at the present, or might reasonably be expected to in the future, interfere with the horse's usefulness. However, whey buying a horse there is usually an element of compromise. You want the horse for a particular kind of riding; you are not interested in a condition that might affect a flat racehorse if you are a dressage fanatic. You may also have financial limitations governing both the price you can pay for the horse and how much you can spend on checking that it is healthy. For this reason, veterinary surgeons in the United Kingdom no longer issue a 'soundness certificate' when they examine a horse. Instead they certify that a horse does not suffer from any conditions 'likely to affect the animal's usefulness' for a specific purpose. There have been people who have suggested that the present certificates are not as useful as the old 'soundness certificates' but that only goes to show that they did not understand the legal definition of 'sound' anyway.

The important point is that you should have the horse vetted before you buy it. This examination is the foundation of your preventive medicine. If you buy a horse with a problem, no amount of prevention in the future can alter that fact. You may be able to cure the problem, but that may involve dire extra expenditure. You may accept that you have to live with the problem, in which case the cost of the reduced performance will be difficult to quantify. It is much better to buy a horse which at the time of purchase does not have any problems which are of significance to you.

The veterinary examination for a purchase consists of five basic parts. First, the horse is examined thoroughly in the stable. Secondly, it is examined at the walk and trot in hand. Thirdly, it is cantered and galloped. Then it is rested before being examined again at the trot. The whole examination takes about an hour or so. In the UK specialised techniques such as X-rays are not usually carried out, although in some other countries they do form a regular part of the examination.

During the first stage of the examination in the stable, the veterinary surgeon will first obtain an overall impression of the horse's general demeanour as shown by its appearance, behaviour and condition and it is studied (as laid down by the Royal College of Veterinary Surgeons) 'methodically, part by part, so that there is no chance of inadvertently overlooking any part'. *Practitioners have their own favourite, precise routine and probably no two veterinary surgeons will do an examination in exactly the same way or order.*

Stage One could be regarded as the most important as early warnings signs may be detected of conditions which can be carefully scrutinised later in the examination. The veterinary surgeon will probably ask that the horse should *not* be worked before his or her arrival as some conditions are intensified or decreased by this process and a false picture can otherwise be gained.

Probably he will first observe the horse from outside the box so as not to disturb it unduly and so get a fairly true picture of the horse's general demeanour when relaxed and unworried. He may look round for evidence of kicking (scarred walls), crib-biting (chewed ledges), quidding if the horse is eating, signs of awkward stance which could indicate a problem or vices such as box-walking, weaving or wind-sucking, although the presence or otherwise of vices is not the area of the examination. The state of any droppings will be noted as an indication of the health of the digestive system.

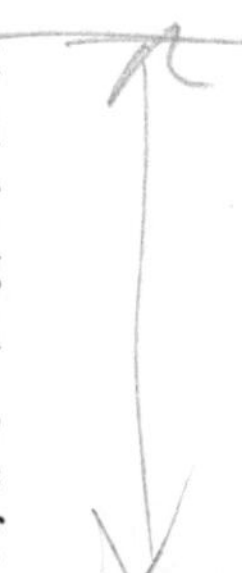

The veterinary surgeon will then enter the box for a thorough 'hands on' examination. He will watch the movements of the horse's flank to assess the character and rate of respiration. Then, using a stethoscope, he will listen to the chest for breathing sounds and listen to the character and rate of the heartbeat. He may also check for bowel sounds to check, once again, the state of the digestion. Although heart rate and pulse are the same, he may also check the rate and nature of the pulse.

Using an ophthalmoscope, the veterinary surgeon will also examine the horse's eyes for any defect of vision and will open and close each eye to see that the pupil contracts and dilates according to the light entering it. (A small torch is also often used for this.)

In Britain, these two instruments are normally the only two used during the examination. However, in other countries, and, increasingly, in Britain, where a need is felt for closer examination, a fibrescope (fibreoptic endoscope) may be used to examine the respiratory tract more closely. This consists of a flexible tube which is passed up one of the horse's nostrils and enables the veterinary surgeon, by means of an integral light, to examine the horse's throat or further down into the trachea. X-ray techniques can also be used, usually on the feet and legs, to detect bone and other changes which may indicate the onset of some disorder in its early stages. However, this can be misleading as an abnormality does not always mean the horse is going to become lame in future and a veterinary surgeon may be in danger of turning down a perfectly serviceable animal which may, in years to come, turn into a world-beater!

Blood tests may also be carried out, both to give information about the horse's health and also as reference which can, if unfortunately necessary, determine whether the horse had been given any drugs prior to the examination. So if a horse goes lame shortly after purchase, this sample can be analysed for pain killing drugs which might have been given to ensure a sound horse was produced to be vetted.

During Stage One of the examination, the veterinary surgeon will thoroughly check the horse's teeth, looking for signs of uneven wear due to crib-biting or excessive wood-chewing and to assess the horse's age. He will also see whether the teeth are under- or over-shot. The cheek teeth (molars) are also checked for sharp edges, broken, decaying or missing teeth, and the state of the mouth regarding cuts and ulcers and gum health is also assessed.

The nostrils will be examined for discharge, blockage or injury and the frontal sinuses tapped to check for the presence of infective fluid which could indicate sinusitis. The lymph glands of the head will be palpated (felt) to check for swelling which could indicate infection, and the horse may be 'coughed' by having its larynx lightly squeezed to make it cough. If a horse has a sore throat due to past coughing, such pressure on the larynx will produce a spasm of coughs, perhaps six or more. The larynx area will be checked for signs of muscle wastage which could indicate laryngeal paralysis, and for scars betraying previous wind operations although these are often difficult to detect. Similarly, lower down the neck, signs of the horse having previously been tubed will be looked for.

The state of the jugular vein, in particular, should be checked as undue swelling here can indicate a heart problem.

Now for the limbs and feet. The veterinary surgeon will run all over the horse with his or her hands, anyway, checking for unusual skin and flesh texture, lumps, bumps, scars and unusual warmth, but the legs come in for particularly close scrutiny.

First, the horse may be moved sharply to each side to check for signs of incoordination, staggering or stringhalt. General muscular development will be checked (atrophied shoulder muscles being a sign of nerve damage), and such things as capped elbow, joint swellings and scars, such as broken knees, will be noted. Each leg is lifted and the joints manipulated looking for signs of restricted movement or pain and stiffness. The condition of the feet is checked, as is their conformation, and the wear pattern of the shoes. The veterinary surgeon will assess whether any abnormalities are natural to the horse, acquired through disease or injury, or the result of faulty trimming and/or shoeing. Defects such as sandcracks or laminitis are also looked for now.

Splints are palpated and their size and position assessed as to whether or not they are going to interfere with the horse's action. The tendons and ligaments are carefully palpated between finger and thumb for signs of fibrosis, heat, swelling and pain. In driving horses, the lateral cartilages are 'sprung' (pressed) to check for ossification (hardening) and pain.

The hindlegs are checked next, although here slightly different abnormalities may be present, such as windgalls and spavins rather than splints. In all legs, signs of ringbone are looked for, and the sesamoid bones just behind and above the fetlocks are felt for heat and swelling. In the hind limbs, the hocks will receive particular attention as being the most common site of trouble here.

The horse will be checked, again, for muscular development of legs and quarters, dropped hip or any bodily unevenness which could indicate lack of use due to previous injury, or nerve damage.

The back (including the spine as far as possible), loins and quarters are palpated firmly for telltale signs of pain. Fibrous, hardened skin and flesh, perhaps due to serious tack or harness injuries in the past, will be looked for as these can cause problems with the fitting and use of equipment in future.

Not until all this has been done, and possibly more, will the horse be brought out of the box for a general assessment of conformation and bodily condition, bearing in mind the client's stated intentions of the use to which he or she means to put the horse. It is no use recommending a Cleveland Bay for flat-racing!

The veterinary surgeon will look at the horse from a slight distance, checking for general conformation, even development, symmetry and, again, the horse's general demeanour, temperament and its response to its handlers and surroundings.

Stage Two of the examination comes next, which involves studying the horse's action during trotting up.

A hard, level surface is needed and the handler must be told to lead up the horse on a loose rope as any tension on it, however minor, can lead to a masking of the horse's true state of going, to the horse's detriment and otherwise.

The horse is first walked towards, past and away from the veterinary surgeon, then back again, then the process is repeated at the trot. It is only at the trot that even slight lameness can be spotted. Only fairly severe lameness is detectable at walk and the canter pace masks all but major lamenesses. Some veterinary surgeons will also ask to see the horse lunged at trot on a hard, level surface in a fairly small circle. This is an additional aid to spotting slight lameness due to the extra and different forces and stresses placed on the limbs and feet on a circle.

There are scientific techniques able to detect lameness, or rather unevenness of gait, invisible to the naked eye, such as gait analysis computer systems and force plate equipment. For such an examination the horse trots over special detector plates or pads and the pressure is recorded and displayed on a screen. This equipment is normally found only in research establishments and university clinics.

As lameness could be described as sufficient discomfort, pain or stiffness to interfere noticeably with the distribution of weight between the horse's four legs, it is difficult to say how important is a lameness which causes no visibly detectable effect on the gait.

The subject of lameness is vast and entire books have been written on that subject alone. For the purposes of this chapter, let it suffice to say that, basically, lameness in a front leg is shown by the horse dropping his head (and his weight) *down* when the *sound leg* comes to the ground, and in a hind leg it is shown when he drops his hip when the sound leg hits the ground. There are all sorts of nuances of this basic rule, depending on how severe the pain is and where it occurs. It may, of course, not even be in the legs but in the shoulder, back, loins, hindquarters or even the neck.

It is not the job of a veterinary surgeon examining a horse for a purchaser to make a diagnosis of the cause of any lameness found. Indeed he has no right to carry out most of the diagnostic procedures which would be required. The vendor must seek advice from his or her own veterinary surgeon if necessary.

Making the horse trot up and down hill is also a useful diagnostic aid to the veterinary surgeon. Trotting uphill, for instance, will bring out knee or hock discomfort whereas trotting down a slight incline will emphasise pain or discomfort in the shoulders and heels of the feet. The sound of the stride can also help; it should be evenly loud. As the diagonal containing two sound legs comes to the ground, it will, because it is carrying more weight, make a louder sound than the diagonal containing an unsound leg. Of course, should the horse be evenly lame in two adjacent feet (rather rare) this is probably best spotted by seeing a shortened, pottery gait.

Stage Three of the examination involves studying the horse during strenuous work. There are cases where this may be impossible, such as in the case of an unbroken animal or where facilities just do not exist for such work. Breeding stock are not normally subjected to this stage of the examination, but, in their case, an extra aspect appears and that is a detailed examination of the breeding organs, which is not carried out on other animals.

The veterinary surgeon requests that the horse be cantered in a circle in each direction for up to ten minutes so that he can listen to the breathing and study its action. Necessarily, the circles should be as small as practicable, with the vet standing in the middle. The horse is next galloped (as close to the veterinary surgeon as he or she feels advisable) at about a three-quarter speed gallop, again for the purpose of checking wind noises and action.

It is then trotted back to him or her and immediately its lungs and heart are checked with the stethoscope to see how they have stood up to work. It should be stressed that the horse need not be physically, athletically fit for this stage of the examination – the purpose is to see how the horse responds to sufficient exertion to make it breathe heavily and put up its heart rate significantly. The fitter the horse the longer this will take. This is not a test of the horse's fitness but of its health – there is a subtle difference.

If the horse is required for jumping, the vet may ask to see it over a fence or two, although this is not strictly part of the examination. It can, however, bring to light problems such as back problems should the horse crab, refuse, buck or take off on landing, although these undesirable behaviour patterns can, of course, be caused by the rider. In driving horses, asking them to pull a loaded vehicle up an incline with one wheel locked often points up back or hind leg discomfort, or sore shoulders.

Stage Four of the examination involves a period of rest. The horse is stabled and untacked, and the veterinary surgeon will once again check its heart and breathing to see if the exertions have emphasised any abnormalities or, conversely, it any previously present appear to have decreased or disappeared. He or she will also note how quickly these two rates return to normal. The rest period usually lasts for 15 to 30 minutes, during which time the certificate can be partially completed, a full description of the horse noted, its name and so on.

Stage Five consists of a further trotting up in hand. The reason for this is that the period of rest may have brought out signs of stiffness or lameness brought on by exercise and not previously apparent.

The examination is now complete.

Sometimes, to save money, prospective purchasers will ask for a partial examination covering simply heart and vision. It is not purely to make extra money that the veterinary profession advises against such partial examinations! There are many potential sources of problems which can cause significant trouble in future but which can only be shown up by a full examination. However, it must be stressed that veterinary surgeons do not have clairvoyant powers. The examination reveals the state of the horse on the day of the examination, not the next day or the one before. Buying any horse is a risk but you can cut your risks considerably by having a full pre-purchase check done. If your veterinary surgeon finds anything which could affect the horse's usefulness in future, he or she can discuss this with you, bearing in mind that no horse is perfect. Some conditions may not deteriorate at all while others may even improve. A full pre-purchase examination is still your best course of action before buying any horse or pony.

If your veterinary surgeon is satisfied with the examination, then he or she will issue you with a written report. This piece of paper is important. It contains a list of every blemish and deviation from normality which the veterinary surgeon observed, whether significant or not. In later months you may be unsure whether, for instance, the horse always used to have two splints on its right foreleg. The certificate is your reference point. Anything which is 'wrong' with the horse now but which was not mentioned on the certificate has come about as a result of your care and your use of the horse.

Never be tempted to buy a horse which has something wrong with it, no matter how convincing the owner's explanation. One has to be cynical about lame horses which must have just been kicked! It is heart-breaking enough not to be able to compete on a horse because it is suddenly taken 'ill', but it is even worse if you knew when you bought the horse that this might happen.

Checking your horse's health

Although a veterinary surgeon's skill and expertise may be needed to detect many of the problems that might be present in a new horse, you should be capable of maintaining that knowledge. In other words, you should make sure that you know how your horse looks and (more importantly) feels to you in normal health. Only then will you be able to spot the very first small signs that something is going wrong. Throughout this book, certain assumptions have been made as to what constitutes normal health but it is hoped that the general pointers in this section will act as a general guide to aspects of recognising good and poor health on an almost daily basis.

Any conscientious owner with genuine feeling for his or her horse will, after owning that horse for a relatively short time, develop almost a sixth sense, an instinct, as to how the horse is feeling.

The general look of the horse, its appearance, will often be the first indication of its health, good or bad.

A healthy, contented horse normally looks bright and interested in the world. Its ears prick towards whatever is holding its attention and can each revolve within a 180° semi-circle. What is more, they can operate independently, a heritage from the days when wild horses and their relatives had to constantly check all round them for sounds (and sights) which could reveal that a predator was stalking up on them with a kill in view.

(When horses are dozing their ears are loosely held to the sides but what may seem like dozing at first glance may, in fact, be sickness.)

The horse's eyes should be bright with a questing, interested look. Unlike the ears, they cannot operate individually but, when the horse's head is held normally they do provide all-round vision, and when the head is down grazing the field of vision is not even hampered by the horse's body mass but only by its four slender legs – an ideal predator-detection device.

The coat, even in a grass-kept or ungroomed horse, should be bright and feel 'lively', and the skin beneath pliant and elastic. Place the flat of your hand on the ribs; you should be able to move the skin fairly easily over them. If you pick up a fold of skin just in front of the shoulder between your thumb and forefinger, it should fall back flat almost immediately in a healthy horse. The skin should carry a bright coat with no rough or bald patches, swellings or tender, sore patches.

The horse's behaviour is also an excellent guide to his state of being. Here, because of horses' differing temperaments (like humans) you must get to know your own horse's behavioural tendencies and peculiarities so you know when his behaviour is abnormal for him personally. If, for example, your horse normally finishes his evening feed within the hour, it will be significant if, one day, part of the food is still uneaten next morning. On the other hand, another horse may never eat up its evening feed but clear up rapidly after a morning feed.

Generally, horses are sociable, so if yours stands away from its companions, looks generally quiet and out of sorts, head down, ears flopping with perhaps dull, sunken eyes, dull, stiff and maybe staring coat with a general air of malaise, suspect trouble. If the horse lies down for more than half an hour at a time, again be suspicious. If he stands at the back of the box unduly looking fed up (and you are certain and honest with yourself that he is not so due to over-confinement) he could be sickening for some disease.

Check on his water consumption, too, as drinking more or less than usual is a good sign that something is not quite right. This is where, if you use automatic waterers, the metered sort come into their own.

During work, always pay attention to how the horse goes. If he seems lethargic, unwilling or difficult, do not automatically get after him but consider if perhaps he is genuinely not well.

When horses roll, they almost always shake themselves when they get up. If they don't it is a sign of possible abdominal discomfort or pain.

A horse's legs and feet should normally feel cool and hard, although there are individual differences. If you do not know how warm or cold they normally feel how will you be able to appreciate that the feet have become warmer due to, say, laminitis? The tendons down the back of the horse's cannons become puffy, warm and swollen when they are sprained. You need to realise that you have a problem at once so that you can rest the horse and allow it to recover rather than carrying on and causing further damage. Different horses' tendons feel different even when they are healthy. So, knowing what another horse's normal tendons feel like is no substitute for familiarity with your own horse. Usually, the tendons and ligaments behind the cannon stand out like cello strings, but not always. What appear to be slightly 'foggy' tendons in one horse may be quite normal in another, although obviously swollen legs due to sprain, lymphangitis or filling due to poor circulation should be obvious in any horse.

The feet should be checked automatically whenever they are picked out; the horn checked and the frog pressed with the hoofpick to check for soreness and a possible horn infection such as thrush, which is also manifested by a dark discharge and foul smell from the frog.

Get to know, also, the state of your horse's droppings. In a stabled horse, they are roughly apple-sized, kidney-shaped balls of khaki colour, of such a consistency that they just break on hitting the ground. In grass-kept horses they are greener and looser. However, they should never be very loose like the consistency of cows' droppings, nor made up of small, hard balls. An unusual colour such as very pale, yellowish or dark is a sign of disorder, as is a bad smell or obvious mucous on the droppings. Most horses pass about eight piles of droppings in 24 hours but check your horse's normal amount so you know when there is any deviation.

The horse normally stands four square on his feet but frequently drops a hip and rests a hind leg, the hoof resting on its toe. If it rests in any other position, or if a forefoot is frequently rested either forwards (when it is known as 'pointing') or backwards, this may be a sign of pain or discomfort in the foot or leg. Resting the foot backwards on the toe can be a sign of tendon or ligament sprain, resting it forwards of navicular disease and standing with the weight on the heels, of course, is the typical laminitis stance.

Signs of colic (general abdominal discomfort or pain) are the familiar ones of looking round at the flanks, snatching at them, rolling and, in serious cases, thrashing about.

General signs of pain and discomfort include patchy sweating, groaning and a frightened facial expression.

If you suspect trouble, and notice abnormal signs, your next step should be to check the horse's temperature, pulse and respiration rates as these are an excellent guide to general health or the onset of disorder.

To take the temperature, use a veterinary thermometer available from your veterinary surgeon (not the finer, more fragile human type), hold it firmly at the top and shake the mercury well down with a sharp snapping movement of the wrist which you will have seen your doctor, and maybe your vet, use. Grease the bulb and part way up the rod with Vaseline petroleum jelly or some other clear, greasy substance, insert it in the rectum (holding the dock towards you with your free hand) and push it *gently* in to two thirds its length with a slight side-to-side, twisting motion. Tilt it slightly to one side to press it against the rectum wall for a true reading (rather than the lower one you would get from inside a ball of dung). Leave it in place for the time stated on the instrument, usually one minute, gently withdraw it (having kept hold of it all the time!) and read off the temperature.

It is essential to take the temperature this way as horses cannot hold a thermometer under their tongues or in their armpits like human beings can. The normal temperature for a horse is around 100.5–101.5°F (38–38.5°C). See Table 1.1. If it is above 102°F (39°C) then the horse is running a fever, although a correspondingly low temperature can also indicate trouble.

Incidentally, do not take a horse's temperature immediately after it has passed some droppings because the reading will tend to be artificially low.

Reading a thermometer is an acquired skill. Make sure that you acquire that skill before you really need it for a sick horse. If you have difficulty buy an electronic thermometer which gives a digital reading. Taking your horse's temperature at rest at the same time every day will give you a clear picture of his normal rate, then you'll know at once if there is a significant variation. The temperature is normally slightly higher in young and unfit animals, lower in older or athletically fit ones.

The pulse and heart rate are the same. A healthy horse at rest has a heart and pulse rate of about 40 beats per minute. The heart rate can be counted using a stethoscope and listening to the chest wall just behind the left elbow. The pulse rate is counted by feeling one of the surface arteries, such as the one which crosses over the lower edge of the jaw just in front of the level of the cheek muscles (Fig. 1.1).

With exercise or excitement the heart rate will increase and may reach 100 to 120 per minute. Although detecting such things as heart murmurs is the province of the veterinary surgeon, you can yourself detect

Table 1.1 Comparison of body temperatures in °C and °F

°Centigrade		*°Fahrenheit*
37.5		99.5
38.0	normal	100.4
38.5	range	101.3
39.0		102.2
39.5		103.1
40.0		104.0
40.5		104.9
41.0		105.8

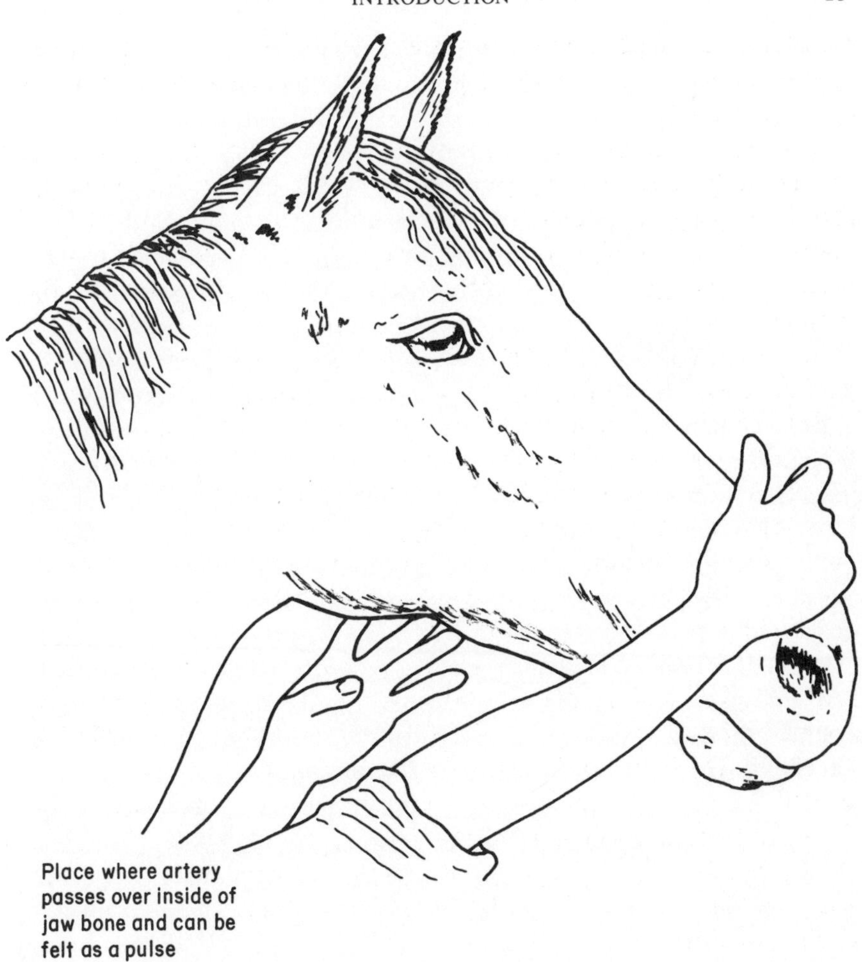

Fig. 1.1 Feeling a horse's pulse.

abnormalities in the nature of the pulse. For instance, familiarise yourself with its usual character, then you can tell whether or not it is abnormally full and 'bounding', or weak.

Respiration can be slightly difficult to check, particularly in a fit, resting horse. Stand behind and slightly to one side of the horse and watch the flank, counting its rise and fall as one breath. A horse usually takes between eight and 16 breaths per minute. Ponies tend to breathe more quickly than Shires, it being a general rule that small animals breath quicker than large ones. Younger animals also breathe more quickly than old ones.

Luckily, you can usually tell whether a horse is breathing quickly because of some disease or lung problem (rather than work) if you compare its respiratory and heart rates. A healthy, resting horse takes, on average, three heart beats for every breath. If that ratio approaches 1:1 then there are definitely respiratory problems.

Body condition (weight carried) is also a good general guide to general health, sudden weight loss or, more unusually, gain both causing suspicion of some disorder. Condition scoring is an excellent method of providing a standard guideline on bodyweight. Remember, also, that some horses are naturaly 'poor', being poor doers or the nervous, highly-strung type, whereas others are naturally good doers, particularly the more stockily-built types. It is important to find out the true type for your horse – under-feeding and then blaming it on the horse's being a poor doer is reprehensible, but just as much blame lies with those who over-feed their animals, get them overweight and prone to heart strain, laminitis, colic and so on and then blame it on the animal's greedy nature!

In condition scoring, cross-sections of the muscles of the pelvic region are considered. If they are convex on either side of the spine, score one. If they are concave, score four or, in extreme cases, five. A healthy horse should have a score of just under three or less.

General signs of underweight are a dip in front of the withers, prominent vertebrae, poor flesh generally, especially quarters, back, shoulders and neck, and clearly visible hips and ribs. Fat horses, of course, are just the opposite, with appley quarters, barrel-like bodies, 'padded' shoulders and cresty necks, often with a 'gulley' running down the spine.

A reasonably fit horse, fit for riding club work, moderate to hard hunting or active hacking should make you aware of his ribs but you should not actually be able to count them! The thighs should meet under the tail but, seen from behind, they should not be wider than the hips. This is a useful general guide to body condition in a moderately hard working animal.

A horse's normal urine is a light yellow colour but, contrary to popular opinion, it is not necessarily clear. Slight cloudiness is quite normal in some horses and is not a sign of disorder. The horse should straddle its hind legs to stale, whether male or female, and a male horse should let down his penis to do so. If he does not, it could be a sign of the sheath being blocked with discharge or of, say, warts or tumours inside the sheath or on the penis itself. Urine which is excessively dark, watery, blood-stained or smelly should alert you to something wrong.

These signs of good health, and otherwise, are not difficult to become familiar with. In time, they should become second nature, and any concerned owner will, as mentioned, know almost instinctively when something is wrong with their horse.

It is always tempting to let things go and 'see how he is tomorrow'. Provided temperature, pulse and respiration are normal and there is nothing obviously or seriously wrong such as persistent coughing, obvious heat, swelling, lameness or abnormal behaviour, not least regarding appetite and water intake, it is not unreasonable to wait for a day or less to see how things progress.

However, if they do *not* improve, and, of course, if they deteriorate, there should be no further delay in calling the veterinary surgeon. This is especially so in cases where the owner is unsure in his or her mind as to what is wrong. Experienced owners should be perfectly capable of administering first aid in the case of wounds and such like, but actual disease, internal disorder of some kind, serious or infected wounds or a general but obvious air of malaise, and suchlike, are definitely the province of the veterinary surgeon. Gambling with your horse's wellbeing is not only grossly unfair to the horse but bad money management on the owner's part, because incorrect first aid, or delay, can so easily result in a more serious condition which will take much more time and money to clear up than if the vet had been called in the first place.

Prevention, or luck?

When something goes wrong with their horse, many owners moan about how healthy some other apparently neglected horses seem to be. This is a smug attitude which completely misunderstands what prevention is all about. For a start, every use we make of a horse introduces its own set of disease risks. For example, a horse standing dejectedly on a roadside tether will not be exposed to the physical forces which may lead to a joint problem such as sprain of a hock. You might say that not subjecting a horse to regular exercise is 'preventing' it from being exposed to a large number of wear and tear diseases. Now if you, like most owners, are going to exercise your horse regularly, then you will have to use different preventive measures to avoid those diseases, such as regular shoeing and the use of a proper training programme. In this book I will be giving guidance on appropriate preventive measures for different situations.

As I have already mentioned, prevention of ill-health costs money and time. Only you, the owner, can say how much you are prepared to pay. If you feed cheap, mouldy hay, you will keep feeding costs low. You will also predispose your horse to both nutritional and respiratory problems.

I do not expect any one horse owner to employ all the measures which will be described in the following chapters. The point I would like to get across is that you should make informed decisions. Only if you know what diseases can be prevented, what measures you can take and why they work in a particular context, can you weigh up the pros and cons properly. In most cases the fact that a horse has not suffered a variety of diseases is more due to luck than to prevention. Keeping your horse healthy is all about trusting to knowledge, not trusting to luck. You haven't the right to gamble with your horse's life and health.

2 Vaccines, antitoxins and how they work

Although this book tries to describe the steps you can take to avoid a whole range of veterinary problems, there is no doubt that when most people think of preventive medicine, they think of avoiding infections. So first of all it is important to have an understanding of what an 'infection' might be. Infectious agents basically fall into four groups; in order of increasing size these are: viruses, bacteria, fungi and parasites such as worms. All these organisms gain entry into part of the horse and live there at the horse's expense. Not all viruses and bacteria cause detectable damage which we would call disease. There are millions of bacteria living on the skin of a healthy horse without producing any visible effect. A skin infection caused by a bacteria called *Dermatophilus congolensis*, on the other hand, will result in rain scald and may affect the skin over the body. The term mud fever is used if it affects the skin of the pasterns or lower leg.

What is a virus?

Viruses are really minute particles. It has been said that they are some two to three thousand times smaller than the smallest speck we can see with the naked eye. They consist of a central core of nucleic acid surrounded by a protein envelope and membrane (Fig. 2.1). Nucleic acid is the basic material of life which is capable of reproducing itself. There are two types of nucleic acid; ribonucleic acid (RNA) and deoxyribonucleic acid (DNA). Viruses have only one sort of nucleic acid present, and so they can be classed as either RNA viruses (such as equine influenza) or DNA viruses (such as equine herpes). I have chosen these two particular

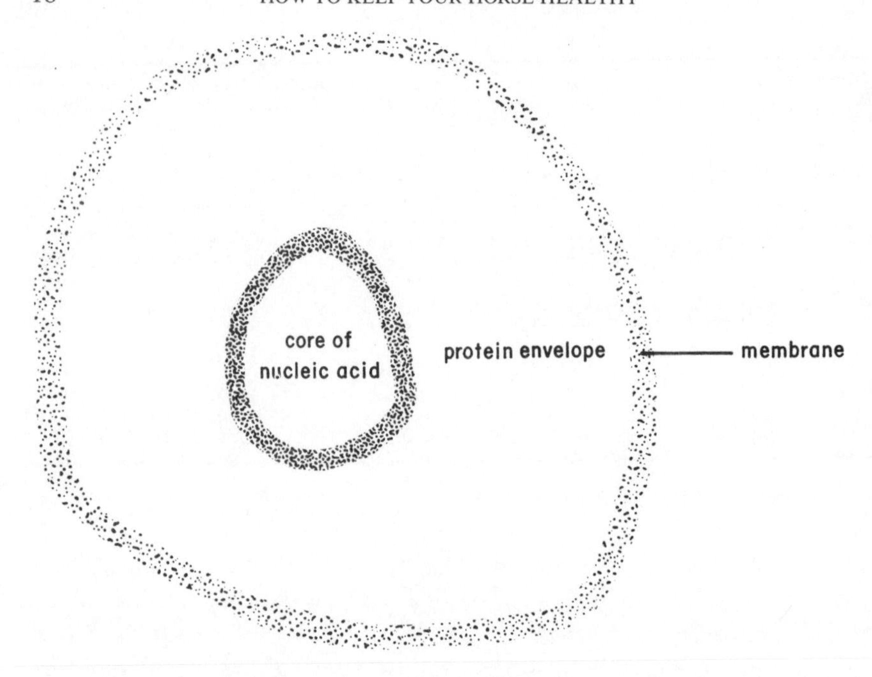

Fig. 2.1 Structure of a typical virus.

examples because they can both cause rather similar respiratory diseases, despite such a major structural difference. They both cause the horse to cough and have a nasal discharge, and laboratory tests are needed to distinguish which virus is causing the symptoms.

Viruses need living cells in which to grow but this does not mean that they cannot survive outside a host. If that was the case they would very soon become extinct because they would die when their host died. Some viruses, such as the influenza viruses, can only survive outside the body for a few hours. This means that in order to survive they must be very infectious; they must be able to establish themselves very quickly. A horse which inhales influenza-virus-contaminated droplets becomes a host as the virus reaches the lungs. Other viruses can survive for weeks or months out of the body. As a general rule viruses can survive cold better than heat. They do not usually like drying, however. (See Fig. 2.2.)

What are bacteria?

Bacteria are about a thousand times larger than viruses, and they can be seen under an ordinary light microscope, whereas we need a very

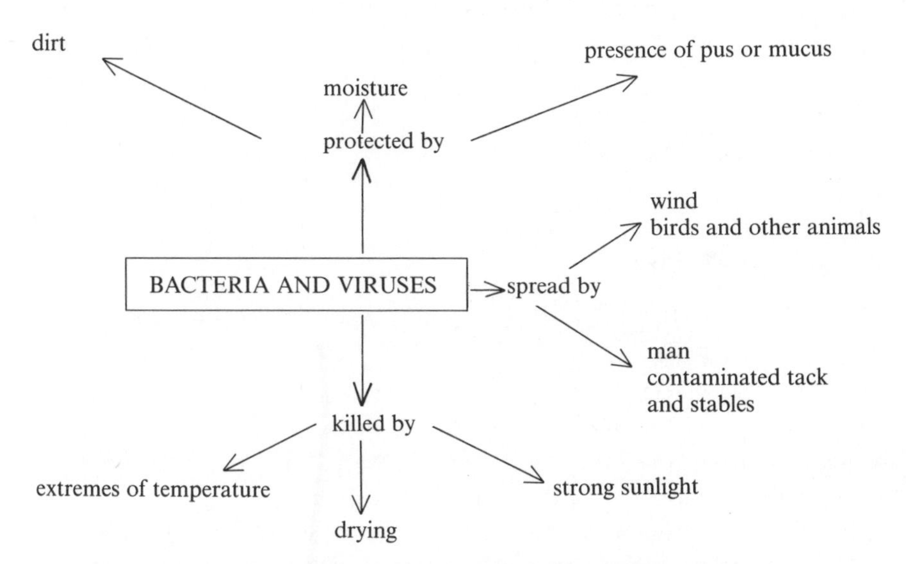

Fig. 2.2 The effect of environment on bacteria and viruses.

sophisticated piece of equipment called an electron microscope in order to see viruses. When we are looking at bacteria under a microscope, we often use chemical dyes to stain the different structures and types of bacteria. Bacteria have a definite nucleus, surrounded by living material called cytoplasm, and a bacterial membrane. One of the first ways in which bacteria were differentiated was by their shape. They may be rod-shaped, e.g. *Esherichia coli*, or they may be round, e.g. *Streptococci* or *Staphylococci*.

Resistance to infection

Infectious agents such as bacteria and viruses are, of course, foreign to the horse. As soon as they gain entry into the horse, the immune system recognises them as being foreign, and reacts accordingly. There are two words with rather overlapping meanings which are used to describe the body's defence. Immunity refers to the state of the body which enables it to resist that particular infection. Resistance to infection includes immunity but it also includes other non-specific defence mechanisms.

A *Salmonella* infection can be used to demonstrate how we use some of these terms. A horse might ingest some *Salmonella* bacteria into its stomach with infected food. The gastric juices are very acidic, and this causes destruction of certain bacteria, i.e. the acidic conditions are part of the horse's resistance to the infection. In addition, the horse may have acquired specific immunity against that particular strain of *Salmonella* bacteria or the horse may have a species immunity against that type of *Salmonella*. In other words it might be a *Salmonella* which can cause disease in, say, dogs, but not in horses.

Antigens and antibodies

The basis of our idea of immunity is the antigen/antibody reaction. Living material (even minute viruses) always contains building blocks of protein and any protein which is foreign to the horse's own body is called an antigen. Antigens are neutralised by proteins produced by the horse itself, and these proteins are called antibodies. Immunity against an infection requires the presence of specific antibodies which can neutralise the antigens associated with the virus or bacteria which cause the disease.

The defensive mechanism which occurs when an antigen first comes into contact with an animal's immune system is complicated. It is worth mastering the various stages, however, because you will then have a much better practical understanding of the problems which might occur in an infected horse. Firstly, the antigen is surrounded, or 'eaten up' by a cell called a macrophage (the word macrophage means destroyer of large things). This process is called phagocytosis. The macrophage passes the information it gains about the 'invader' to a white blood cell called a β-lymphocyte. These lymphocytes may then develop in one of two ways. They may change into memory cells, which will enable the horse to mount a much quicker and more active response if it comes in contact with the same antigen on some future occasion. Alternatively, the lymphocytes may develop into plasma cells, which actually produce antibodies and release them into the bloodstream to neutralise any other particles of the same antigen which might be present (See Fig. 2.3.)

Lymphocytes are manufactured in the bone marrow, which, inciden-

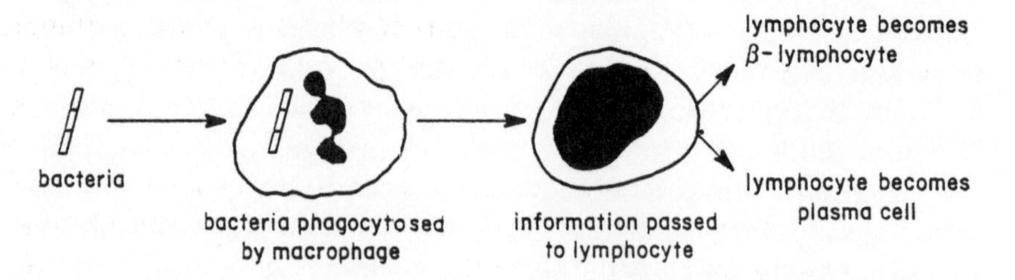

Fig. 2.3 How white blood cells respond to a new infection.

tally, is why people with bone-marrow disease sometimes need a marrow transplant from someone else before they can fight any infections. Once having been manufactured, the memory cells and plasma cells gather together in the lymphoid tissues. In respiratory disease the areas of lymphoid tissue in the roof of the horse's pharynx (at the back of its mouth) may become enlarged and possibly cause coughing.

Lymph nodes are scattered throughout the body. These become enlarged when stimulated by infection. The lymph nodes most easily felt when enlarged are those on either side of the horse's throat. By causing slight pressure on the larynx, or voice box, they too may cause coughing. As long as there are sufficient numbers of memory cells present, the lymph nodes close to the entry point of an infection may enlarge very quickly. There is, however, no stimulus to encourage them to reduce to their normal size and it is not uncommon for the glands around the throat to remain enlarged for weeks, or even months, after a respiratory infection.

Antibodies often react in a characteristic way with their antigen, which may be of value in testing for the existence of the disease which is associated with that particular antigen. An antibody which reacts with a soluble antigen may result in the production of a fine precipitate or powder. An antibody which reacts with a larger antigen particle will cause the particles to clump together, or agglutinate. Figure 2.4 shows how an 'artificial' antibody made against the antigen associated with the horse's defence against the *Strongylus vulgaris* worm can be used to show by agglutination whether the horse has a worm problem or not.

The antibodies which a horse produces are called immunoglobulins, i.e. they are proteins of the globulin type which are involved in immunity. There are three main types of immunoglobulin in the horse, each acting in a different way. The immunoglobulin IgM is associated with the initial response to the infection. IgG is associated with the much more rapid response to further exposure to the same problem. Both IgM and IgG are present throughout the body, being transported via the bloodstream. IgA is a more local defence, and is found on surfaces where infective agents might try and gain entry. This has considerable practical importance when you try to develop a vaccine against respiratory infections in horses. IgA may be important in stopping viruses from penetrating the horse's body in the first place.

Many conventional vaccines, unfortunately, stimulate relatively little extra IgA production even though they may stimulate considerable amounts of IgM and IgG production. So the vaccines tend to be less effective than they might be. Another point about IgA is that it is less

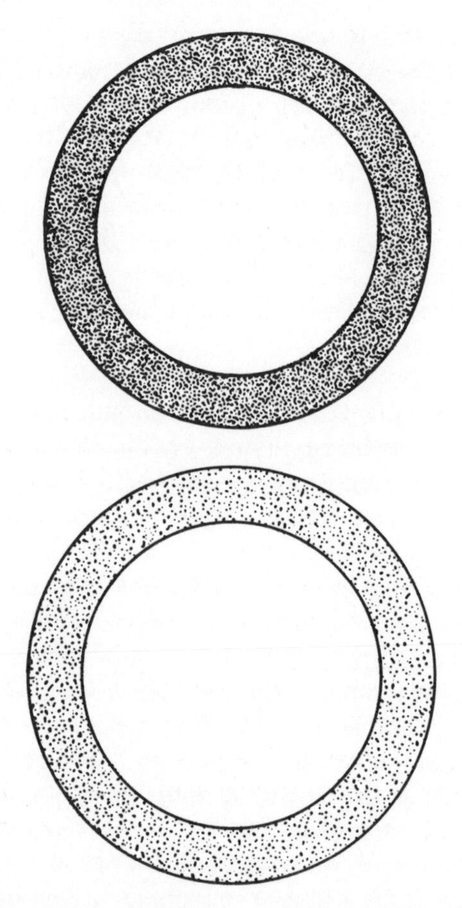

Fig. 2.4 An antibody/antigen agglutination test. Notice the particles in the top ring, which has agglutinated, compared with the negative agglutination in the lower ring. (*Courtesy Cambridge Life Sciences Ltd.*)

specific than the other two types of immunoglobulin. So if we can raise IgA levels by repeated vaccinations against one respiratory virus, for example equine influenza, there is some evidence that the IgA will make that horse less susceptible to other respiratory viruses such as the herpes viruses.

Hypersensitivity

So far, everything we have considered about the horse's immune system has seemed beneficial. Sometimes, however, the body over-reacts. When this happens it is called hypersensitivity. The commonest example in the horse is hypersensitivity to the dust, especially fungal spores, in hay and straw, which produces chronic obstructive pulmonary disease (COPD) or broken wind. Hypersensitivity is due to lymphocytes producing an antibody which, when it reacts with its antigen, causes the release of chemicals such as histamine from the white blood cells. The histamine released in the lungs of a horse with COPD causes constriction of the airways, and so difficulty in breathing.

Passive immunity

No discussion of the process of immunity would be complete without a consideration of 'passive immunity'. This is the situation where the animal is given antibodies from another animal rather than having to produce its own. When a foal is born it has no antibodies at all, even though the hostile world is full of bacteria and viruses waiting to invade it. The mare's colostrum, or first milk, contains high levels of antibodies against all the diseases to which the mare has immunity. As long as the foal drinks an adequate quantity of colostrum during its first 24 hours of life, it will absorb these antibodies directly into its own bloodstream. From 18 hours after birth onwards, however, the amount of immunoglobulins which are absorbed falls rapidly. It is therefore essential to (if possible) bottle-feed a new-born foal with colostrum during its first few hours of life if it will not suck, rather than leave it to suckle for itself from 24 hours old onwards. It also follows that if a mare loses her colostrum because she runs with milk for days or weeks before foaling, then the foal will have greatly reduced immunity.

Passive immunity can also be obtained whenever a horse is given antiserum, e.g. against tetanus toxin. The antiserum contains large amounts of antibodies 'harvested' from a blood donor horse. Such antibodies are relatively short-lived. Because they are foreign to the horse which receives them, and lack its own characteristic genetic 'thumbprint', they will be destroyed after about three weeks by the horse's true immunity system. In the meantime, however, they will hopefully have served their purpose and prevented the disease.

The theory of vaccination

Armed with the knowledge we now have about how a horse's immune system responds to an infection, we almost expect to be able to manufacture a vaccine against every common disease. Each of these vaccines should:

(1) Effectively prevent clinical signs of the disease, stimulating an immune response at least as good as that which follows the natural disease.
(2) Produce a long lasting immunity.
(3) Be safe and free from side-effects.
(4) Be stable during storage etc.
(5) Be economic in price.
(6) Be unaffected by the presence of any passive immunity in the foal from its mother.

I have deliberately listed the attributes of any ideal vaccine before even defining what a vaccine is. We often know what we want before we find the solution to a problem. A vaccine is a vehicle which allows the introduction of an antigen into the horse in such a way that it will stimulate the active production of antibodies and other immune responses against a specific infection.

There are three main ways in which vaccines can be administered. They may be given orally, as is the case with the polio vaccine for humans, given on a sugar lump. There are no horse vaccines given by mouth. Vaccines which are aimed at protecting against respiratory infections, where local production of IgA is, as we have seen, quite important, may be given intranasally. At the present time there are no intranasal vaccines for horses, although there are intranasal vaccines against virus respiratory diseases for cats and cattle. It might well be that in the future this route might be used in horses. Finally, vaccines may be given by injection. To minimise the risk of a local reaction to the vaccine, horses are usually vaccinated intramuscularly rather than subcutaneously, as is done in dogs, for instance. The horse's skin appears to be very sensitive to foreign substances such as vaccines, and all too readily forms a hard swelling at the injection site. The first vaccine ever marketed against equine influenza, for instance, caused an unacceptably high percentage of such reactions and was withdrawn. A recent survey of reactions following the vaccination of horses against equine influenza and/or tetanus showed that reactions are much more likely to follow the use of a combined vaccine against the two diseases than the use of a vaccine against just one of them. Paradoxically, the better the vaccine is at stimulating immunity, the more likely it is to cause such a reaction. Vaccine manufacturers have to strike a delicate balance in such matters when developing commercial vaccines.

Live and dead vaccines

Vaccines fall into two main types, depending on how they are prepared. Live vaccines contain the actual infectious agent against which you want to protect. The viruses or bacteria are, however, treated in such a way as to remove completely their ability to cause disease. This process is called attenuation. One way in which this is achieved is to collect bacteria, say, from a clinical case and multiply it many, many times in the laboratory. From among the many slightly different strains of bacteria which are produced, the one which causes fewest clinical symptoms is selected and the process repeated until the ideal vaccine strain is found.

Dead vaccines are manufactured using the normal clinical strain of the organism which causes the disease. The bacteria or viruses are then killed using either heat or chemicals. They must not be destroyed in a way that alters their chemical structure because that would alter the way they acted as antigens compared with the live organism.

Let us now return to the situation whan an antigen enters the horse's body. The aim of vaccination is to produce good levels of antibody and a strong immunological memory so that if the actual disease should come along then the so-called 'secondary response' will occur very rapidly, producing a high level of new antibodies. A single dose of dead vaccine produces only a small amount of antibody, and primes the memory cells. So at this stage the amount of protection provided against the disease is very small. When the body has assimilated this primary reaction, which will take at least 14 days, and in the case of some horse vaccines may take much longer, a second dose of dead vaccine has to be given. This stimulates a much higher level of antibody production, thanks to the already primed memory cells. Of course, in time even this antibody is lost from the system due to natural wastage. A booster injection of vaccine then needs to be given to restore antibody levels (Fig. 2.5). Even the natural immunity which the horse produces in response to clinical disease varies in how long it lasts depending on which infection was involved. It is not surprising, therefore, that the period of time which can be allowed to elapse between booster vaccinations will vary from infection to infection. It may even vary according to which manufacturer has prepared the vaccine.

When a live vaccine is used, it also triggers off the primary response. The vaccine organism continues to live on inside the horse, however, so that it is still living there quite happily 14 days or more after the vaccination. The vaccine organism is therefore also able to stimulate the secondary response. So a single dose of live vaccine can produce a high

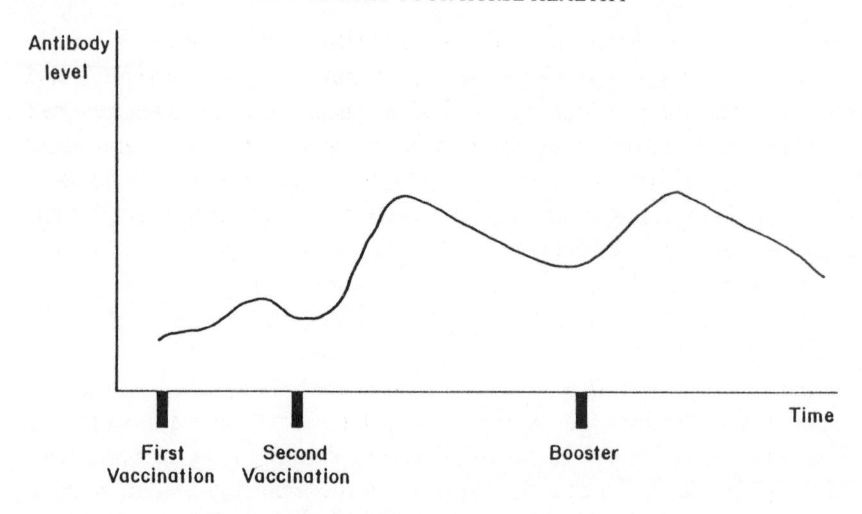

Fig. 2.5 Typical antibody response to vaccination.

level of antibody production. The live vaccine organism may further help antibody stimulation by multiplying within the horse.

At first sight then, all vaccines should be live if at all possible. Not surprisingly, however, this immunological efficiency is achieved at a cost in other directions. Live vaccines almost invariably produce side-effects which are similar to the effects of the infective organism. Such effects are rarely as severe as those produced by a clinical infection, after all there would be little point in using the vaccine if they were. Nevertheless, the vaccine may well produce a temporary fever, and in pregnant mares this may well cause abortion. The point about such vaccine-produced symptoms is that they are the result of a conscious human decision. Owners of horses which suffer a severe side-effect may suffer a financial loss, and although it is possible to remind them that they might have suffered even more as a result of a natural infection, it is not guaranteed that they would have done so. They might have had only very minor symptoms. So the temptation to seek to recover a financial loss from those who advised them to use the vaccine and those who manufactured it is very great.

There is a further major difference between live and dead vaccines. After an injection of dead vaccine, there are no live organisms in the horse. None can therefore escape into the environment from the horse, and so there is no chance that a non-vaccinated horse in contact with a vaccinated horse can become 'infected' with the organism. A live vaccine organism may escape into the environment. So an in-contact horse may receive a dose of live vaccine, whether its owner wanted it to do so or not.

Every time the vaccine organism reproduces itself, either inside or outside the vaccinated horse, there is also a chance that it might change back and regain its ability to produce true clinical disease. There may even be a risk that such an active organism might exist in the vaccine in the first place. Whilst it is possible to guarantee that every organism in a dead vaccine has been killed off, it is very much harder to be sure that there are no 'rogue' viruses in a live vaccine.

Adjuvants

One way in which dead vaccines are made more effective is to use adjuvants. These are chemicals which are incorporated in the vaccine in order to produce a greater antibody response. There are a number of substances used as adjuvants, and it is not unusual for different manufacturers to use different adjuvants and make great play of the different properties these confer on the vaccine. Some adjuvants, such as aluminium hydroxide or water-in-oil emulsions, are thought to allow only a gradual release of the antigen into the body, so producing an effect something like the continuing activity of live organisms. Other adjuvants may actually stimulate the vaccinated animal's immune system. Once again, though, these advantages are gained at a cost. Adjuvants can cause local reactions at the site of the injection. It is often the case that the more effective the adjuvant is immunologically, the more likely it is to cause a tissue reaction around the injection site.

Practical aspects of vaccination

Whatever kind of vaccine is used, the dose is always the same no matter what the purpose of that particular dose. Many people appear to be under the impression that a different preparation is used for booster vaccination than for the primary doses. This is not the case: a syringe full of vaccine might be used for a first dose in one horse or for an annual booster in another. Another misconception is that the size of the animal affects the dose of vaccine. This is not the case: the same dose volume will be used in a Shire stallion as in a six-month-old Shetland. This is because a certain minimum antigenic mass is needed to trigger off the equine immune system, but once that system has been triggered off then injecting a larger antigenic mass will not result in significantly higher levels of immunity. Antigenic mass, incidentally, refers to the actual amount of protein in the vaccine which is the specific protecting antigen. Vaccines from different manufacturers might vary in the antigenic mass which they present to the horse's immune system.

Despite differences in the preparation of the antigen for a vaccine, and in the adjuvant used, the vaccines from different manufacturers are interchangeable in respect of a vaccination programme. If the primary two vaccinations use vaccine A, it is quite safe to use vaccine B for the first booster, and then switch back to vaccine A. The immunity which the horse has at any time will generally be related to the last vaccine used. So if vaccine A stimulates longer-lasting immunity than vaccine B, the immunity after that first booster will be shorter lasting even though the primary course used vaccine A. One exception to this interchangeability of vaccines occurs when attempting to protect against a disease organism which has several different strains. In such cases different manufacturers may make different choices as to which strains to include in their vaccine. This will obviously have some effect on the resistance to the disease following vaccination. The equine influenza vaccines marketed by different manufacturers, for example, contain different strains of the equine influenza virus.

There is some evidence that although giving a greater antigenic mass during vaccination may not stimulate greater antibody levels, giving more doses of vaccine may do so. This certainly appears to be the case with equine respiratory virus vaccines. The vaccination programmes sometimes used in young Thoroughbreds in training for racing owe part of their logic to the fact that the full immunological response to a vaccine may be only short lasting, and may soon fall, and partly to the fact that as a result of the programme they will have a relatively large number of doses of vaccine. This is also typified by the official Jockey Club equine influenza vaccination rules in the United Kingdom, which require the initial two doses of vaccine to be followed by a third, after five to seven months, before extending to annual boosters. This compensates for the fact that the initial vaccine may not last as long as one would like. It also ensures that even two- and three-year-olds will have received three or four doses of vaccine.

In theory it is difficult to over-vaccinate, but in practice problems can arise if a horse is vaccinated too frequently. The problems usually stem from stimulating immunity to contaminants found in the vaccine or, worse still, to other parts of the vaccine, e.g. the adjuvant. Tetanus vaccine is particularly susceptible to this problem, and doses of tetanus vaccine should not be given more frequently than once a year. It is an unfortunate fact that 'dirty' vaccines may cause more reaction but higher levels of immunity than 'clean' vaccines which cause little or no reaction.

The new-born foal is perfectly able to respond to antigens (whether from a disease organism or not) and produce effective immunity. Nevertheless at birth the foal has almost negligible amounts of antibody present, so that by the time a full immunological response could take place over three or four weeks, the foal might be long since dead from the disease. Instead of transferring vital immunity against disease to the foal before birth, the horse does this via the colostrum, as discussed earlier. As a result a three-day-old foal may have antibody levels as high as its mother. If, however, we attempt to vaccinate such a three-day-old foal, we get no response at all. The maternal antibodies from the mare destroy the vaccine antigen. With the passage of time the maternal antibodies decay. They cannot be replaced, and so by three to six months of age a foal has no maternal antibodies. If we now attempt to vaccinate the foal, we get a normal response.

So we do not usually attempt to vaccinate foals before they reach three months of age. This is not because the foal cannot respond to the vaccine before this, but because the vaccine may be blocked by maternal antibodies. Adopting a rule of thumb like this inevitably means that in a number of foals there will be a susceptible period between diminished maternal antibody and the vaccination. The only way to avoid this is to take regular blood samples from an individual foal and measure the levels of antibody against the particular disease which concerns us. When the antibody levels drop, then it is worth starting the vaccination programme, no matter what age the foal is at the time. Needless to say, a foal which does not receive any colostrum, perhaps due to the death of its dam, will not have any maternal antibodies either to protect against disease or to block vaccination. Unfortunately some foals which appear to have been reared normally with neither receive nor absorb sufficient antibodies from their mare's milk and will be at risk. A simple agglutination test, similar to that already described, can give a quick and easy estimation of the immunoglobulin levels present in the foal's blood at three or four days of life, i.e. after it has stopped absorbing antibodies from its mare's milk but before it has had time to manufacture any of its own. Some insurance companies operating in the expensive Thoroughbred world now require evidence of adequate immunoglobulin levels before they will insure a foal.

As part of our efforts to ensure that foals have effective levels of protective antibodies, we need to make sure that the mare's colostrum has high levels. For relatively 'uncommon' diseases this is best achieved by vaccinating the mare during late pregnancy so that her blood antibody levels are boosted when she is manufacturing her colostrum. Common infections from the environment can be just as dangerous to a new-born foal as influenza etc., and to ensure that the mare also has good protection against the common infections to which the foal will be exposed, the mare should spend at least the last 14 days of her pregnancy at the stud where she is going to foal. Sending the mare away to foal only a few days before foaling may save money, but involves a risk to the foal. It also follows that if a mare does foal unexpectedly at home, it is best to wait as long as possible before sending the mare away to be served again, so that as many as possible of the foal's most susceptible early days will be spent in the environment for which it has been given some protection.

Returning to the question of vaccination in general, we now frequently use combined vaccines which protect against several diseases at once. There is a degree of competition for the immune response when combination vaccines are used, but this can usually be safely overcome by balancing the different components. Combined equine influenza and tetanus vaccines are very widely, and effectively, used.

Coping with changes in a disease

The organisms which cause disease sometimes try to overcome the body's defences by appearing in a number of very slightly different antigenic forms, or strains, of the same organism. Where the variations are relatively minor, then an effective vaccine against one will still protect against the other. If the variation is more distinct, then a vaccine will only work if it contains antigens from the particular strain which is causing trouble on this occasion.

A disease organism may gradually change during the course of an outbreak due to natural mutation etc. This is sometimes called antigenic drift. Where this drift is substantial, vaccine manufacturers may have to re-think the components of their vaccine. As a result of antigenic drift during the various outbreaks of equine influenza in Europe during the years immediately following 1979, slight changes have been made in the vaccines used. Interestingly enough the vaccine manufacturers have overcome this problem in different ways, as I mentioned earlier. One has introduced an A Equi/2 (Kentucky 81) component into their vaccine, for instance, whereas another has introduced an A Equi/2 (Fontainebleau 79) component.

Failure of vaccination

Even when a horse is vaccinated with the correct and effective vaccine, there is no guarantee that the horse will never suffer the clinical disease. The horse may suffer from an immuno-deficiency, i.e. due to a fault in its make up it may be incapable of producing normal antibodies. At the present time there is much discussion in human medicine of the disease AIDS (acquired immune deficiency syndrome), which is caused by a virus and which often causes death because the patient cannot fight off an infection of some kind. Immuno deficiency in the horse is usually hereditary, and so it is in foals that evidence of the disease is shown (they would not usually survive long enough to become adults). There is also some evidence that resistance to infection may be less than it ought to be in horses which are severely malnourished. This makes sense, because in such a situation no body system will work at maximum efficiency. Resistance to disease is also reduced in horses which are in poor condition for other reasons, and in horses which are very old. So if we consider the life of a horse, at birth it has practically no immunity. During the first few years of life its immunity against common diseases should be adequate. Repeated exposure to these diseases means that by the time of physical maturity, its resistance should be very strong due to frequent 'natural vaccination'. Only at the very end of its life do a horse's overall resistance levels drop. Not surprisingly, many attempts have been made to find ways other than vaccination which will stimulate a horse's immunological system. There is a drug called levamisole which is thought to stimulate an immune system which is not working as actively as it should, although it has little or no effect in a normal animal. The drug is given orally and has two actions: it stimulates the lymphocytes and increases phagocytosis. There are no specific studies showing that levamisole also works in horses, but it is quite widely used. Care should be taken not to overdose with levamisole because there are reports of toxic doses being given in other species of animal. It should never be given by injection, as although this latter way of administration is safe in cattle it can cause serious side-effects in horses.

Antitoxins and antisera

No consideration of the use of vaccines would be complete without a look at the use of antitoxins and antisera. First of all, an antitoxin is a fluid containing high levels of protective antibodies against a disease. These antibodies are prepared in one animal for administration to another. Horse antitoxins (and some antitoxins for use in humans or other species) are prepared by repeatedly vaccinating a horse until it produces really high antibody levels. Blood is then collected from that horse and treated to remove the blood cells and platelets, leaving just the immune globulin proteins behind. As their name implies antitoxins contain antibodies against a bacterial toxin rather than the bacterial organism which releases it. Tetanus anti-toxin is the most commonly used antitoxin. Antisera are made from the serum (that is the fluid part of the blood without the blood cells) of horses which have high antibody titres, or levels, against an actual organism. There are no commercially available antisera for use in horses in the UK.

Antitoxin acts immediately. There is no waiting for the horse's immune system to do anything. Antitoxins provide passive protection, i.e. the horse's body remains passive and needs do nothing. Of course, the horse's body doesn't necessarily remain inactive. Even if we give antitoxin to a horse which has been infected with tetanus, the horse will start to produce its own antibodies. The question is whether it will live long enough to complete the process. Generally speaking, antitoxins and antisera are prepared to protect against diseases which have a very rapid and serious effect.

The immunity provided by antitoxins is very short-lived. The horse's body recognises that they are of foreign origin, having been made by another animal and not by itself. It accordingly manufactures antibodies to neutralise the antitoxin antigens. So within about three weeks (the time taken for immunity of any kind to develop, whether to a disease or vaccine) all this passive protection has been lost. By that time, though, the active immunity should be working sufficiently to take over its job. Many horse owners have to have a dose of tetanus antitoxin given to protect their horse because it has suffered a wound etc. Months later when it has another wound they think it will still be protected 'because it had a tetanus jab last time'. This is not the case. Only through a proper course of tetanus vaccine (called tetanus toxoid) can immunity be achieved which will last more than three weeks.

So antitoxins and antisera are emergency measures used in the face of an immediate threat. Almost without exception you should never have to resort to their use. If a disease is serious enough to justify considering the use of an antitoxin, it is serious enough to justify a proper preventive vaccination programme. The exceptions would be a very recently purchased horse, whose vaccination history you do not know, and a horse which had definitely been exposed to an exotic disease which did not usually occur in that country.

In this chapter we have been very much concerned with a horse's immunological response to a particular infection, and what we can do to improve its immunity to that specific organism. This is not, however, the whole story of resistance to disease. As I mentioned earlier, resistance is a much wider concept.

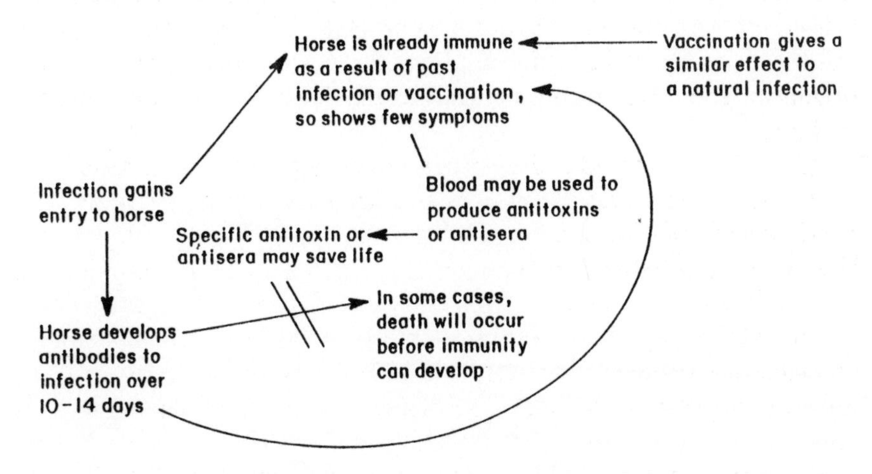

Fig. 2.6 Summary of Chapter 2 – infection and immunity.

3 The horse's natural defences

The spread of disease

The antigen/antibody reaction is central to an animal's attempts to stay healthy and free from diseases. It is, however, only part of the broader canvas of resistance to infection. The surest way to stay free from trouble is to place a safe distance between it and your horse. Some disease organisms cannot live away from the horse at all, and so can only spread if an infected horse comes into direct or short-lasting indirect contact with an uninfected horse. This need for direct contact is the mark of what is called a contagious disease. Lice are contagious. They can only spread by one horse rubbing against another, or by it rubbing against another object which the uninfected horse rubs against within a very short time. Here we also come across one of the mechanisms which the contagious organism can use to get over the disadvantage of not surviving away from the horse. The lice irritate the horse's skin, causing it to rub, and this rubbing given the lice a chance to spread. Even a short distance is sufficient to keep a horse safe from a contagious disease.

Many infectious organisms, on the other hand, have at least a limited ability to survive during the spread from one horse to another. This means that we can consider there to be a circle of varying radius around each infected horse, and any other horse coming within that circle is at risk of contact with the infectious organism. The big problem from the point of view of keeping your horse healthy lies in knowing what that radius of danger is. To some extent it will depend on the means used by the disease organism to survive away from its original host. Respiratory infections usually survive by being associated with a tiny droplet of mucus which is breathed or coughed out into the open air. These droplets are only slightly heavier than air, and so stay suspended in the atmosphere for some time before settling. Coughing obviously projects the infected droplet some distance (another instance of the disease causing a symptom which helps it to spread). Meteorological conditions then come into play. Wind will carry the droplets further before they are deposited. Hot sunshine, however, will dry up the water droplets, and the disease organism, quite rapidly. Respiratory infections can travel large distances and still infect another horse. See Fig. 3.1.

When human beings take a foreign holiday, the combination of unfamiliar food and unfamiliar bacteria often results in gastro-enteritis. The symptoms of vomiting and diarrhoea will be all to familiar to many people. Horses can also suffer from infections of their alimentary tract. For all practical purposes horses do not vomit (although they can do so when they are extremely ill and near to death). They can, however, have diarrhoea as a result of a bowel infection. Foals, like all young animals, are particularly liable to such problems. The actual diarrhoea often contains many millions of the bacteria etc. which are responsible for the illness. So as the horse moves around it spreads the disease organism and increases the chance of the infection being picked up by another horse.

A horse with diarrhoea may well, therefore, be dangerous to other horses which graze with it, even if there are relatively few horses in the paddock. On the other hand, if the same horse is stabled it will not pose a threat to any other horses because they will not come into contact with the infected diarrhoea. There is, however, an exception to this statement. Even if a horse is stabled, it can still come into indirect contact with a susceptible horse. This happens when some other agent carries small particles of the infected faeces directly to another horse. You, the stable owner, are the most likely indirect threat in such circumstances. Human feet pick up infected material and deposit it elsewhere. The means of indirect spread of disease can either be another living creature, such as men, rats or birds, or it can be an inanimate object such as grooming kit etc.

Practical aspects of quarantine and isolation

The question of disease spread is obviously a complicated one, and the safety zone which one needs to keep between an infected and an uninfected horse varies tremendously. In earlier days quarantine and isolation were the only ways available to limit disease spread. The two

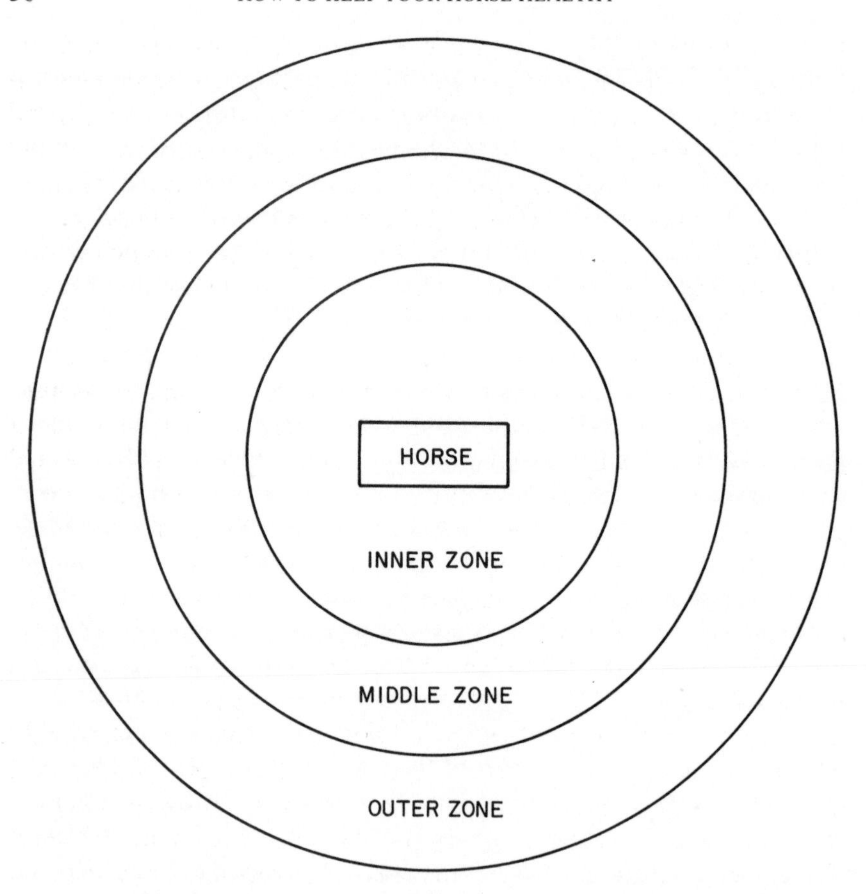

INNER ZONE: Lice and other parasites cannot travel away from the horse; they need close contact

MIDDLE ZONE: Bacteria and viruses which can survive in water droplets can be carried distances of several hundred yards

OUTER ZONE: Viruses such as African horse sickness which spend part of their life in an insect (in this case the mosquito) can be spread over hundreds of miles by wind borne insects

Fig. 3.1 The zones of risk around an infected horse.

words, quarantine and isolation, do have distinctly separate meanings, although they are often used to mean the same thing. Isolation means placing the affected animal away from any others. Quarantine, on the other hand, implies that the isolation is imposed on you by outside sources. So you mught decide to keep a horse in isolation when it returns from a show where there seemed to be large numbers of horses coughing. If, however, you were importing a dog into the UK from abroad the law would force you to keep it in quarantine for six months on arrival. By and large the British authorities try to avoid quarantining horses on arrival in this country. They prefer to insist on their quarantine being spent in their country of origin. At the present time horses being imported into the UK from the USA have to be quarantined for 30 days in America before they are allowed to enter this country. This is to reduce the risk of infectious viral arteritis entering this country, where it does not at present occur.

People often ask why horses returning to the UK from overseas do not have to be quarantined to ensure that they are free from rabies, as most mammals have to be. The answer is that an animal is only quarantined if there is a risk of it spreading the disease to susceptible animals. Infected horses do not spread rabies to other animals by uncontrolled biting etc., and so are not considered to pose a significant risk. Quarantining incoming horses may not, in any case, secure sufficient protection for other horses within that country. African horse sickness, for example, is spread by an insect and so could theoretically 'escape' from a quarantine station. So no horses at all are allowed into the UK from countries where African horse sickness has occurred during the last two years.

As our horses are often exposed to infectious diseases away from home whilst competing in various disciplines, it is worth considering the sort of isolation facilities which might be used on their return in order to ensure that they do not spread any disease to other horses in the yard. Remember, incidentally, that if you used your own horsebox to bring your horse home, that is now infected and so should not be used for any other horses until it has been washed, disinfected and dried as I will describe later. Anyone hiring out vehicles to transport horses must by law clean and disinfect them at the end of every journey. The percentage that do so is exceedingly small, however, because except at large cattle markets there are no inspections carried out to check that they have done so.

Isolation premises should be as far away from other horses as possible. It has been said that you cannot really isolate horses with respiratory virus diseases because the infected water droplets can be carried so far on the wind. At least a quarter of a mile in distance is needed to give any real isolation against such infections, and even this is often too little because birds etc., can still give indirect spread. Isolation premises should ideally be downwind of other horses rather than up-wind. A final point to make here is that one man's isolation can be another man's infection. We have to consider the morality of isolating an infected horse a quarter of a mile away from your other horse, or horses, if it means placing it nearer to your neighbour's horse than it would otherwise be.

Isolation premises should be self-contained in every respect. There should be sufficient food of all kinds, including hay, to last throughout the whole period of isolation. Similarly there should be enough tack, grooming kit, etc. to enable you to work the isolated horse as much or as little as you wish without having to 'borrow' from healthy horses. Every trip to fetch and carry risks making a nonsense out of all your efforts at isolation. Ideally, therefore, you should have a completely different person looking after any horse in isolation, someone who never comes near the other stables at all. In practice this cannot often be achieved due to shortage of manpower, money or both. However, it is possible to minimise the degree of risk involved in transferring from yard to yard. If the person changes vehicles where necessary, and wears a clean 'coverall' (of the type sold in do-it-yourself shops) whenever at the isolation premises, then the body area that can be carrying disease will be very much reduced. There should also be a pair of rubber boots that can be cleaned and used exclusively at the isolation premises.

Isolation premises should obviously be constructed in such a way as to be easily cleaned. Apart from anything else, you do not want the present inmate (who may only be there as a precaution) catching the disease which affected the previous occupant. Easy cleaning means having as few nooks and crannies as possible, and having walls and ceilings which are impervious to moisture. In many instances this can only be achieved by having cement-rendered walls etc. which have been gloss painted. This naturally adds to the cost of an isolation facility, which might not be used very often. There is, however, little point in not doing the thing properly.

Cleaning and disinfecting

At this juncture it is worth giving some thought to the question of cleaning and disinfection. The two must go together. A layer of dirt, faeces and dust can easily shield bacteria or viruses lurking beneath it from some or all of the effects of a disinfectant. Not only that but some disinfectants, such as the hypochlorites, are chemically inactivated by the presence of organic, i.e. living, matter. Such disinfectants have their effectiveness drastically reduced by the presence of faecal material etc. So thorough cleaning is the first step.

Vacuum cleaners can be put to extremely good use in the stable. They remove dust and dirt without throwing it up into the air to possibly spread further, which is what happens during brushing. When all loose matter is removed we can wash all the surfaces, including ledges, beams and ceilings which are above eye-level. Hot water tends to dissolve muck better than cold water. A detergent may also make cleaning easier. Here again you must be careful because some disinfectants are affected by some detergents. Thorough rinsing afterwards should solve this problem. It will also compensate for the fact that you will almost certainly not change your washing water often enough and end washing with a detergent/muck soup. Pressure hosing or steam cleaning are very efficient methods of cleaning, so see if you can beg, borrow or hire the right equipment (Fig.3.2).

Drying is quite an effective way of killing bacteria and viruses. In fact some people use disinfectants totally ineffectively yet achieve the desired result unwittingly, through allowing a drying-out period afterwards. So

Fig. 3.2 Pressure hosing or steam cleaning.

thorough washing and drying will, of itself, drastically reduce the numbers of potentially dangerous micro-organisms present in a stable etc. Many people are also under the impression that cold kills off these organisms as well. They often say 'what we need are a few sharp frosts to kill all these bugs off'. Many of the organisms can, however, survive cold quite well. It is a general rule that heat kills bacteria etc. more effectively than cold. Even so a very high temperature may be needed, and it may need to be maintained for at least 10–15 minutes. Boiling instruments, etc, in water will take at least 15 minutes to sterilise them, and even then will only work if the instruments were clean in the first place. Surgical instruments are usually sterilised in a form of pressure cooker called an autoclave. This reaches temperatures very much higher than normal boiling point because the whole system is under pressure and water boils at a higher temperature when under pressure.

How to use antiseptics and disinfectants

It is important to draw a distinction between an antiseptic and a disinfectant. An antiseptic prevents bacteria from multiplying and developing, but does not necessarily destroy them, whereas a disinfectant does. Antiseptics do not usually kill living tissue, and so they can be used on wounds etc. without causing any damage. Nevertheless, antiseptics are wider ranging in their effects than antibiotics, which merely affect bacteria of specific kinds, depending on the antibiotic used, and do not kill any of the horse's own cells.

A disinfectant always destroys the physical structure of a bacteria or virus. Because they are so toxic to living tissues, they cannot be used on wounds etc. Some disinfectants, such as the hypochlorites, have their activity reduced by the presence of other living matter, e.g. faeces. Others, such as formalin, do not.

There are a number of disinfectants which are of value in disinfecting stables etc. The cresol group of disinfectants, which are manufactured from coal tar, are effective against bacteria and viruses. A solution of 4% lysol will kill practically everything, but it must therefore be handled with great care. A 2% solution of lysol can also be used to disinfect tack etc. This group of disinfectants is not affected by the presence of other organic matter. Washing soda is not quite as effective, and needs to be used as a very hot 4% solution. It kills both bacteria and viruses. Disinfectants should always be used at the strength recommended by the manufacturers. If they are used on wet surfaces, then they will be instantly diluted, and will not be at the correct strength. Similarly, even if they retain their effectiveness in the presence of organic matter, a dirty solution is a 'diluted' solution.

Fumigation

Fumigation is really disinfection by gas. The usual agent used is formaldehyde, which is liberated by heating paraform tablets. For fumigation to be successful the stable must be made as airtight as possible, even to the extent of using sticky tape around the window and door frames. The stable is then left sealed for a period of several hours. The exact length of time depends on the agent used. Fumigation is not cleaning. The stable will be just as dirty afterwards as it was before, so cleaning should always precede fumigation.

Time and its effects on infections

In addition to isolation by distance, one must also consider isolation by time. As a general rule, the cleaner the premises, the shorter the period for which infectious agents will survive because they are less likely to be protected by dust and dirt from drying, ultra violet light and temperature changes. Viruses tend to survive for shorter periods in the environment than bacteria. Fungi, especially the ringworm fungus which can be so troublesome in horses, survive a much longer time. This is because they form spores which are specially designed to survive away from the host animal. Ringworm spores can survive for many months in stables, on tack and even on the horse's skin. This enables the disease to survive from year to year. Because ringworm often flares up in the winter, runs its natural course and is then not a problem in the summer time, people have thought that either grass or sunshine had a therapeutic effect. This is not the reason why we see less ringworm in the summer. The spores are still surviving. However, those which are in the wood of the stables etc. are no longer in contact with the horses, and grazing allows sufficient distance between horses for the disease not to spread if it does cause clinical symptoms.

What is an incubation period?

The other problem with time and infections lies with the concept of an incubation period. This is the period which elapses between a horse coming into direct physical contact with the infectious agent and the development of the first noticeable symptoms. In most cases there is not a precise incubation time, even for each specific infection. One might, however, expect that the incubation for most virus infections is measured in days, whereas with ringworm it might, as has been mentioned, be several months between the fungal spore 'landing' on a horse's skin and it starting to multiply and cause bald areas.

The incubation period tends to get shorter and shorter as a disease outbreak progresses. This is thought to be due partly to the organism literally becoming more infectious as it multiplies more and more frequently. It is also a reflection of the fact that whereas the first horse in the yard to start coughing as a result of a virus might have coughed out tens of millions of viruses as a potential threat to other horses, if ten horses were coughing at the same time there would be hundreds of millions of viruses released. The chance of a healthy horse breathing in some live viruses would obviously then be much increased.

Horse owners often find out too late that their horse has been in contact with another, already infected horse. They then spend an anxious time waiting to see whether symptoms do develop, and they naturally would like to know when the danger period is over. The incubation period of most bacterial and virus diseases is usually between three and ten days. If a horse has not shown any symptoms within 14 days of returning from the race or event where contact might have occurred, then it is reasonably safe to assume that it will not do so.

There is, of course, another factor which also affects this. As we have already considered, it takes about 10–14 days for antibody levels to be raised sufficiently to provide protection. So if a virus has entered a horse's body on day 1, even if the virus is still alive at day 14, it will usually have stimulated enough immunity by then to stop any further problems. There will always be the odd exception to the rule, especially in the early stages of the spread of a disease when the incubation period is at its longest, but two weeks of isolation is a good basis on which to work.

The horse's general defences against infections of all types

If, despite all your efforts, a virus or bacteria does come into contact with your horse, the horse has some general defence mechanisms. These non-specific defences are in addition to the more specific antibody/antigen reactions already discussed. The greatest defensive barrier is the horse's skin. Bacteria may live on the skin, but because they have no access to the

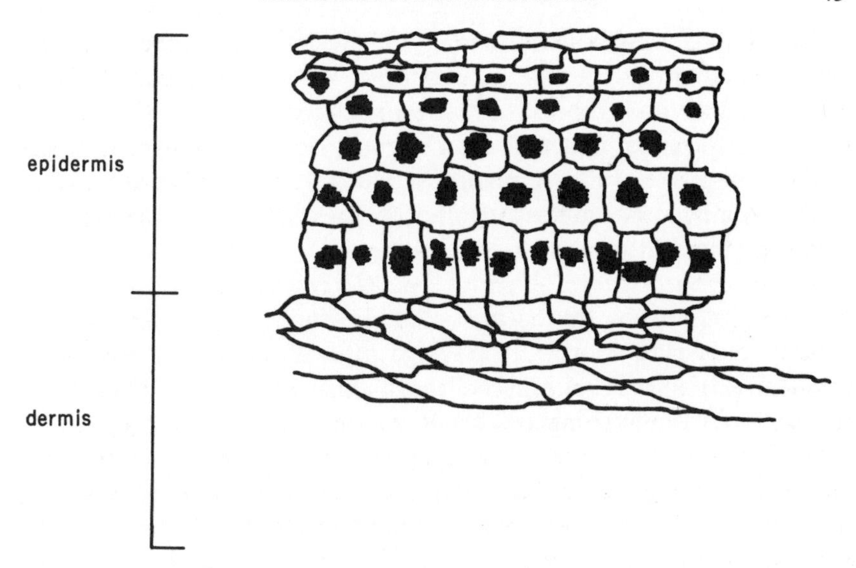

Fig. 3.3 The layers of the skin.

bloodstream they do not have any effect on the body as a whole. Some organisms, especially *Dermatophilus*, can cause skin infections, but these are in a minority.

The reason why the skin is such a barrier, even when we have clipped off all a horse's coat, it is that the top layers of cells are dead (Fig. 3.3). In fact the bottom layers of cells are constantly dividing and making new cells to replace the dead layers which tend to rub off. So if rhinopneumonitis virus were to land on a horse's skin, it would have to burrow through several layers of dead cells, hardened with a chemical called keratin, before it reached any blood vessels etc. If a horse has badly fitting tack, where it rubs it will remove the protective keratinised layers of cells. Bacterial infections then have a much easier job establishing themselves.

Anyone who has had a horse which suffers from mud fever (a bacterial skin infection caused by the *Dermatophilus congolensis* organism) may have noticed that the quality of the barrier to infection provided by skin can vary. Skin which grows white hair is always much more likely to become infected than skin which contains pigment. There does not appear to be any difference between skin which grows chestnut hair or black hair, etc., as long as it has some pigment present. It is thought that this weakness is a direct result of the presence or absence of a chemical called melanin, which produces all the colour variations. It may well be that the traditional prejudices against a horse with four white socks is associated with the relative 'sensitivity' of such skin. Nor is mud fever the only problem associated with white socks. A condition called photosensitivity also usually affects white rather than pigmented skin. Photosensitivity is a type of sunburn. Blisters form on the skin when an affected horse is exposed to direct sunlight, and the skin becomes very red and inflamed. A number of plants found in pasture, especially St John's wort (and, in the US, klamath and buckwheat), can make the horse hypersensitive in this way.

Although the surface layers of dead keratinised cells make skin basically waterproof, this barrier is not impregnable. Anyone who often has his or her hands in water of varying temperature knows how their skin can suffer. In the case of horses, the skin of the lower parts of the legs is often wet for long periods from puddles and streams during exercise. If you do not take care to dry the legs when you return from exercise this period of soaking will be even further prolonged because the hairs of the coat will hold moisture on the skin rather like a wet sponge. In time the top skin cells will absorb water, swell up and soften. They are then much less able to fulfil a protective role. Cold temperatures speed up this whole process, and further lower the effectiveness of the horse's local immunity against *Dermatophilus*. This is why mud fever is so common on the lower parts of the legs during the cold, wet winter months. White skin is particularly susceptible to problems of this kind. Paradoxically the same infection can cause problems in hot, dry weather. In this case the dust etc. 'sandblasts' the top skin layers away and allows the bacteria entry to the deeper layers. This condition can be more difficult to prevent than mud fever, even though it has the same cause. If you keep a horse's legs as dry and clean as possible, and clip away the hair which holds moisture and stabilises scabs etc. then mud fever can be controlled. There is no way, however, of preventing the sandpapering effect of hot dust. It is true that ointments such as Vaseline and certain barrier creams can help keep the organism away from the susceptible skin. Unfortunately, if any organisms have already gained entry, you are just sealing them in and ensuring they have a warm, sheltered environment in which to multiply.

The horse is therefore at its most vulnerable wherever there is a break in the skin. So the eyes, nostrils, mouth, rectum, vagina (in the mare) or sheath (in the stallion or gelding) are the obvious routes for an infection to gain entry. Many of these ports of entry are lined with a variation of skin called a mucous membrane. This is basically skin without the dead, keratinised cells but with extra secretory glands, etc. which stop the mucous membrane drying out by secreting a continuous film of moisture. Once a bacterium or virus lands on the surface of a mucous membrane it has warmth and moisture, the two main requirements for its survival. In some cases the body can close off the opening using a set of sphincter muscles, which act rather like a purse-string. The rectum is usually closed in this way, except during the time when the horse is actually passing its droppings, and few infections can gain entry by this route. The eye, on the other hand, is open most of the time, and infections carried on fine dust particles can come into contact with the mucous membranes. Even here, however, there are very strong muscles which will close the horse's eyelids and seal off the eye if the horse is aware of any threat. Anyone who has tried to hold a horse's eyelids open will know just how strong these muscles are.

Normally the lips of a mare's vulva are closed except when she is passing urine. The physical character of the small amounts of mucus on the mucous membranes of the vagina usually keep it free of any infections unless they are specifically introduced on the stallion's penis during mating. Occasionally a combination of poor conformation, slack muscles and damage at previous foalings results in a faulty seal. Air (contaminated with dust and bacteria) can then be sucked into the vagina (Fig. 3.4) and infections can establish themselves. It would appear that where the angle of the vulval lips is less than 50° to the horizontal, they will almost certainly gape open at some stage. So anyone considering purchase of a broodmare should always look at the angle of its vulval lips and not buy any mare whose lips are more horizontal than this 50° angle. Mares which 'wind-suck' in this way do not necessarily show any symptoms, incidentally. There may well be no trace of a vulval discharge. Nevertheless, chronic infections may make the vagina very inhospitable to stallion sperm, which cannot survive in the infected mucus, and the mare may prove very difficult to get in foal.

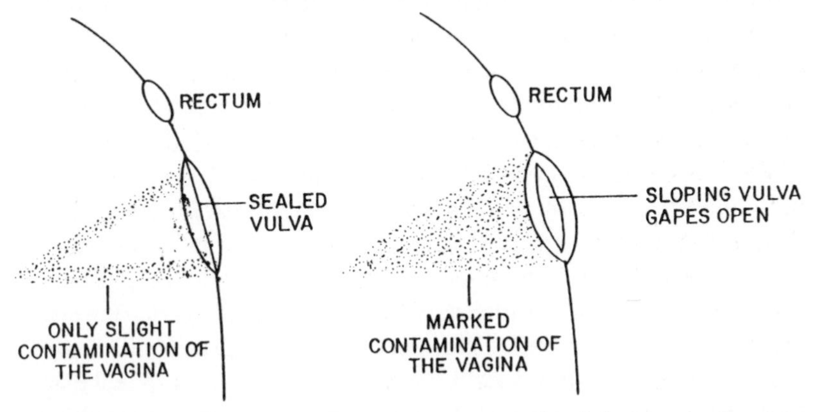

Fig. 3.4 How the conformation of the mare's vulva can allow infection to gain entry to the vagina.

The two main routes by which infections gain entry into the horse's body are via the mouth and via the nostrils. I will deal with the whole question of the respiratory system in the next chapter. The mouth takes in soil, grass, rust, dirt, water. It also takes in many bacteria and viruses. The saliva and gastric juices make sure that the contents of the stomach are kept completely acidic. This low pH destroys the walls of most of the bacteria and viruses. Nevertheless, some of them have developed the ability to survive in such a dangerous environment. These organisms can then multiply within the alimentary tract. In most species of animal, bowel infections result in vomiting and diarrhoea. The horse, however, cannot readily vomit because it has a relatively small and tight valve at the entrance to the stomach (which is, of course, the exit for the vomit). Diarrhoea can, however, occur in the horse. Perhaps the most potentially dangerous bowel infection in the horse is that caused by *Salmonella* bacteria.

There are literally hundreds of members of this family of bacteria, each one different in some subtle way, and each one stimulating a specific antibody response from its host animal. In the horse *Salmonella typhimurium*, *Salmonella enteriditis* and *Salmonella anatum* are particularly troublesome. *Salmonella* bacteria are so well adapted to living in the intestines, alongside the harmless bacteria which are always present in large numbers, that a carrier state often develops. By this I mean that the *Salmonella* bacteria live and reproduce for long periods (perhaps years) but never cause any symptoms of disease. If there are sufficient numbers of bacteria, some will be carried with the horse's faeces to the outside world. Here they may infect other horses, but this time they may cause a disease state rather than a carrier one.

Whether *Salmonella* bacteria cause disease or not depends on whether the horse they enter has protective amounts of antibody present (perhaps from a previous encounter) against the precise strain which is presenting the challenge. The interesting thing is, however, that it also depends on other, non-specific factors. So *Salmonella* can cause disease in perfectly healthy horses, but more often than not it only affects foals, horses in very poor condition, and those which have been stressed. Stresses such as travelling, lack of food, anaesthesia and surgery have all been associated with severe salmonellosis and diarrhoea. It is thought that in these situations the body's natural defences have been weakened. This is partly due to alterations in the levels of those normal 'acceptable' bacteria in the bowels and partly due to suppression of the actual immune response.

Diarrhoea is in itself a protective mechanism, being basically just a speeding up of the rate of passage of food and faeces along the bowels.

The aim is, of course, to get rid of potentially dangerous substances quicker than would normally be the case. This is why we see diarrhoea as a response to several different situations. Toxic poisons, such as arsenic and some insecticides, can cause diarrhoea, and so can some poisonous plants, bacteria, viruses and too much food. The less time the bacteria spend in the body, the less opportunity there is for them to cause lasting damage. Because the gut contents pass through much quicker than normal, less fluid is absorbed back into the body than normal, which is why diarrhoea is so wet. It is true that in some circumstances fluid is taken from the body stores and lost into the bowels, but by and large diarrhoea is rapidly-moving gut contents first and moist second (and not the other way around). In other words, the failure to absorb fluid which would normally be absorbed is the main cause of dehydration with diarrhoea.

You can always have too much of a good thing, and this certainly applies to diarrhoea. Although basically a protective mechanism, a horse is more likely to die of dehydration from diarrhoea than from the activities of the infection which caused it. Nor is it just water which is being lost. Vital chemicals such as sodium, potassium, chlorides and bicarbonates are also lost. So if a horse does develop diarrhoea without any obvious cause (I say that because eating lush spring grass will cause diarrhoea but will not need any treatment) then it might be worthwhile taking immediate steps to try and prevent dehydration. There are several proprietary brands of electrolyte mixtures now available for horses. If these are not obtainable, then 1 oz (28 g) of salt should be added to each gallon (4.5 litres) of drinking water as a temporary measure. Horses will drink such salty water quite readily, especially if the salt level is increased gradually over the course of a day or so.

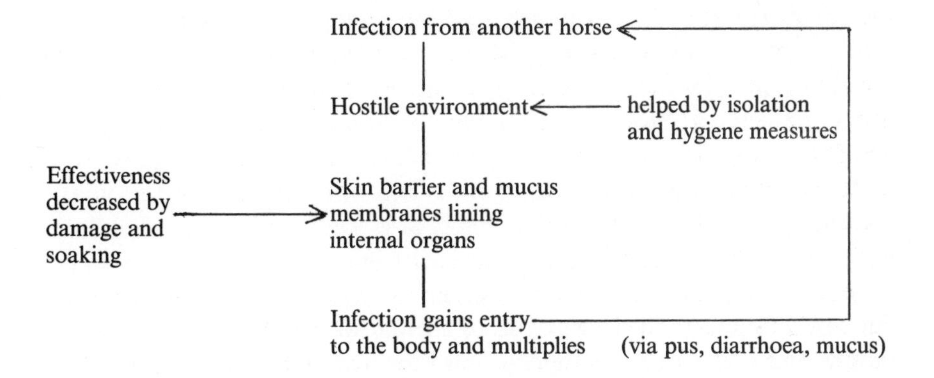

Fig. 3.5 The spread of infection.

4 Avoiding respiratory disease

Over the past few years horse owners all over the world have often asked why we seem to suffer more problems with the respiratory system of our horses now than we used to in the past. Like so many questions, it is easier to ask than to answer. We are asking more of our pleasure horses now than we used to do, and so the limitations placed on their performance by respiratory disease are more noticeable. It is also true that our horses are now more mobile than they used to be. Children's ponies may compete several times a week during the school holidays, at venues dozens of miles apart. Racehorses jet from one continent to another for a race lasting a few minutes, and then fly home again. Every time a horse meets other horses, especially those it has not been in contact with before, it has the opportunity to pick up a respiratory disease (or to pass on to those other horses a disease which it already has). Another significant factor in the present incidence of respiratory problems is that our standards of horse management have not risen, and may have actually fallen in modern times. In that phrase horse management, incidentally, I include the way we make hay and other feeds for our horses and the types of stable we keep them in.

Respiratory problems tend to fall into two categories, infectious diseases and others. We can further divide the infectious diseases into those caused by viruses and those caused by bacteria. There is a great deal we can do to avoid respiratory infections. The general measures I have already discussed to prevent the introduction of infections into your stable yard are especially relevant in this respect. The main diseases also have specific characteristics, however, which require specific counter measures.

Infectious respiratory diseases caused by bacteria

Strangles (sometimes called distemper in the USA) is a particularly virulent bacterial disease. It is caused by the *Streptococcus equi* bacterium. When the infection establishes itself in a horse it localises in the lymph nodes, the glands whose job it is to trap infectious agents and neutralise them. The lymph nodes associated with the respiratory system are most likely to be involved, although sometimes the glands inside the abdomen are infected (the disease is then often referred to as 'bastard strangles' because it produces different symptoms). The glands become very swollen as they literally fill with pus. In some cases they cause respiratory distress because the swollen glands restrict the horse's airways.

Horses with strangles run a very high temperature and are thoroughly miserable. They often have a copious discharge of pus from their noses, and the pus-filled lymph nodes may burst, discharging pus through ulcerations in the skin. These symptoms have a great bearing on how the disease spreads. The discharge, whether from the nose or the ulcerated lymph nodes, is infectious because it contains live bacteria. These bacteria can survive for some time after they leave the horse, protected from drying etc. by the pus around them.

The most important step to prevent the spread of strangles is to isolate any infected horses. As I have explained, the disease is spread via the relatively 'heavy' discharge rather than in small droplets floating in the air. So affected horses do not need to be isolated by any great distance from other horses, but scrupulous attention must be paid to ensure that no drops of discharge are carried on clothes or tack (including grooming equipment) to unaffected horses.

Strangles stimulates very good immunity, which lasts for a relatively long time, so it is usually a disease of young horses rather than adult horses. This is partly because older horses have some resistance. It may also be due to the mixing together, which often takes place, of young horses who may not be in the best of condition. It is quite possible to vaccinate against strangles, and in the USA a number of vaccines are available. In Great Britain no such vaccines are produced, because the incidence of the disease if not considered high enough to justify the pharmaceutical companies' overheads.

Perhaps the major reason why the incidence of strangles has decreased over the past few decades is that, as a bacterial disease, it can be controlled by the use of antibiotics. There is a special consideration involved when deciding whether to use antibiotic therapy in a horse with strangles. Killing the bacteria with drugs will reduce the chances of spread of the disease by reducing the infectious discharge released. The horse involved, however, may end up with lymph nodes which are still swollen because they have now been able to wall off the pus rather than burst. For this reason there has sometimes been an unwillingness to use antibiotics in treatment until any swollen glands have actually burst. Where there is little chance of any further spread of the disease this point may be worth considering. In very early cases and whenever the horse's life is threatened, antibiotics will always be used.

Another infectious respiratory disease caused by a bacterium is known as rattles or summer pneumonia and is caused by the bacterium *Rhodococcus (Corynebacterium) equi*. It normally affects foals between two and four months of age so, although not widespread, can cause severe problems on an affected stud, particularly as it tends to recur in subsequent years, possibly from previously infected dust or soil.

The disease responds best when caught early but is difficult to spot and by the time symptoms develop (breathing difficulties, coughing, swollen glands, poor appetite, a slightly raised temperature and sometimes infected eyes) the outlook is poor, about 66 per cent of affected foals dying. Abscesses can form in the lungs and ulcers in the digestive tract, and, although these can be identified by X-ray or ultrasound scanning, by the time this stage is reached the foal will almost certainly die.

Treatment with antibiotics is generally indicated but the bacteria quickly become resistant. Aggressive therapy with some of the new antibiotics may prove successful, but this needs to be prolonged and it is expensive.

Prevention is difficult as the bacteria are present wherever horses are kept. It is not clearly understood why some foals (and studs) become affected sometimes year after year while others do not. There is no vaccine. There are other diseases caused by bacteria which are infectious and affect the respiratory tract and sometimes other systems as well but they are so uncommon as to be outside the scope of this book.

Conditions such as pneumonia, pleuritis (pleurisy), pharyngitis, bronchitis, laryngitis and suchlike are normally secondary infections closely following or accompanying a primary infection, in other words they are complications.

Infectious respiratory diseases caused by viruses

It is the viral respiratory diseases, however, which most people are frightened of. We sometimes talk as if these diseases are a modern invention; after all, horse trainers in the 1940s and 1950s didn't blame 'the virus' every time a fancied horse was beaten. Viruses may cause more trouble now than they used to do because our horses move around more and so spread infections more widely. Nevertheless if we look at blood samples taken years ago and stored in a freezer, or at wild ponies which do not really come into contact with our pleasure horses, then we can still find plenty of evidence of the presence of respiratory viruses. So these viruses are not just a modern problem.

There are a number of viruses which can affect the horse's respiratory stystem, but perhaps because of their odd-sounding names, horse owners have often lumped them together as 'the virus'. Two of these viruses, the equine influenza virus and the equine herpes virus (type one), need to be considered in detail. The other viruses, including adenoviruses, picorna viruses and rheoviruses, tend to have symptoms which are very similar and may indeed be treated as a group. For example, these less important viruses cause relatively minor symptoms such as a clear nasal discharge and a slight cough. On their own they cause few problems. When they infect a horse which suffers an infection with influenza or herpes virus at the same time, though, they may make the symptoms of the mixed infection more serious than if only one infection had been present.

Equine influenza came into the horse world's knowledge when the virus was isolated from an outbreak of respiratory disease in Prague in 1956. This strain of the virus is known as Equine Influenza A type 1 (Prague). The other major strain is Equine Influenza A type 2 (Miami). There are other strains but they vary only marginally from one or other of the main strains. This is in marked contrast to the situation with human influenza, where there are literally dozens of strains of virus, each one antigenically distinct.

Coping with equine influenza

The symptoms of equine influenza are basically the same whichever strain is involved. The horse runs a fever for up to four days. During the early stages there is a dry cough, a relatively unusual feature of respiratory infections, which more usually cause a moist cough. There is also a nasal discharge; clear and watery at first but gradually becoming thicker and more mucous in character.

Before we can look at ways of avoiding infection with equine influenza, we need to look at the danger points of the infection. First it is an extremely infectious disease which can affect 100% of a susceptible group of horses. The cough may sound dry, but it is still projecting thousands of virus particles, protected from drying by a tiny mucous droplet, into the atmosphere. Equine influenza can occasionally be fatal, especially in young foals and older horses. The virus can cause permanent damage to the muscles of the heart and to the liver. It may take three or four months for the horse to completely recover from the damage to these organs, even though it only coughs for a week or so.

As there is no cure for equine influenza, prevention by vaccination is to be strongly recommended. All horses on the premises should be vaccinated, not just those which are going to shows etc. It has been accepted that for a vaccine to work most effectively, at least 80% of the population need to be vaccinated, and each stable yard is its own mini population in this regard. Leaving some horses unvaccinated may save money (equine influenza vaccination is not cheap) but these unprotected individuals might contract the disease from a virus brought home by you or other horses. Once they become infected they multiply the numbers of virus particles in the air thousands of times, and the point may be reached where there are so many virus particles that they overcome the immunity of some of the vaccinated horses in the yard.

In the United Kingdom there are two types of vaccine available against equine influenza. They are both inactivated vaccines; there are no live equine influenza vaccines. One contains equine influenza A Equi/1 (Prague), A Equi-2 (Miami) and A Equi/2 (Kentucky 81) strains of the virus. The other contains the A Equi/1 (Prague), A Equi/2 (Miami) and A Equi/1 (Fontainebleau 79) strains. Originally the vaccines contained only the Prague and Miami strains of the virus. At the end of the 1970s, however, there was a severe influenza epidemic, and during the thousands of times when the virus spread from one horse to another, and the millions of times that it reproduced itself, there was some degree of 'antigenic drift'. In other words, the antigenic make-up of the virus was slightly altered in some cases. It was still equine influenza A Equi/2 but not necessarily completely identical to the Miami strain. Once these changes had been confirmed, the World Health Organisation Reference Laboratory for equine influenza recommended that vaccine manufacturers should widen the cover provided. Manufacturers differed in their opinions as to which was the best strain of virus to add to their vaccine in order to do this. From the horse owner's point of view there seems little difference in the efficacy of the two types of vaccine.

A further difference between the vaccines is that one is water based and has no adjuvant present, the other is saline based and has an aluminium hydroxide adjuvant. All the vaccines, incidentally, have an adjuvant incorporated when they are combined with tetanus toxoid vaccine. Adjuvants, as I have mentioned in an earlier chapter, may make the vaccine more powerful as a stimulator of antibody production, but there is a possible risk of some reaction in the horse's body around the vaccination site. The very first commercial equine influenza vaccine was eventually withdrawn because it produced a higher level of local reaction than was considered acceptable. It has been suggested that the 'cleaner' the vaccine, i.e. the blander the liquid base of the vaccine and the less adjuvant present, then the more difficult it is to make the vaccine effective.

As I have already explained, it takes more than one dose of an inactivated vaccine to stimulate reliable immunity. There has been considerable confusion over the vaccination programme necessary to produce this effect with equine influenza. The major disparity is between the minimum vaccination programme which will be accepted by official bodies and the programmes recommended by the vaccine manufacturers. It might be easier to understand why there is any disparity at all if we look at the reasons behind their formulation. The vaccine manufacturers must draw up a vaccination programme which is comprehensive enough to protect a horse even in circumstances where only a small proportion of the horses are vaccinated. It must also be appropriate for all ages and classes of horse and pony. The regulatory bodies, however, are formulating a programme for a very different situation. Because the programme will be compulsory, 100% of the horses at official events will be vaccinated. At the same time, horses which are involved in competitions might be expected to be of above average fitness and health anyway.

Looking first at the vaccination programmes required by the various bodies which regulate equine events, the basis is the requirements of the Jockey Club. These are as follows:

> All horses should receive two injections for primary vaccination, given no less than 21 days apart and no more than 92 days apart. Horses foaled on or after January 1st 1980 should have received a first booster no less than 150 days and no more than 215 days after the second injection of the primary vaccination. Booster injections should then be given at intervals of not more than a year apart (although for horses foaled before January 1st 1980 then any boosters given before March 16th 1981 may have been given at intervals of not more than 14 months). Horses should not receive any of these injections within 10 days prior to them entering the racecourse premises.

If a horse is vaccinated in such a way to fulfil these requirements, then they will almost certainly satisfy any other compulsory requirements. The vaccination programme outlined above is, it must be stressed, only a minimum requirement. The vaccine manufacturers suggest one of two, more comprehensive programmes. For the vaccines containing the equine influenza A Equi/2 (Kentucky 81) strain, an initial two doses of vaccine separated by four to six weeks should be followed by a first booster six months later and a second booster six months later still. Further booster vaccinations should be given annually thereafter. With the vaccine containing equine influenza A Equi/2 (Fontainebleau 79) the initial two doses should again be separated by four to six weeks. The next two doses should again be given at intervals of six months. After these, however, booster vaccinations are recommended at nine-month intervals. The manufacturers also state that horses at high risk to infection (e.g. racehorses in training and competition horses) can be vaccinated at intervals of six months if required.

The manufacturers not only differ over the vaccine make-up and on how often boosters should be given (and in the racing world horses have even been vaccinated at monthly intervals), they also differ in other respects. One manufacturer warns that vaccination should not take place immediately after exercise or transportation. They suggest that after the basic vaccination injections, severe physical exertion, training or transportation should be avoided for seven days. After booster vaccinations they suggest that horses should not undergo severe exertion for two or three days. Other manufacturers do not feel it necessary to give any warnings about the use of their vaccine in stressful circumstances. The manufacturers do not explain why there is this difference, but are convinced that they are right and the others wrong. There have certainly been circumstances where horses have become off-colour after vaccination, and owners or trainers of horses undergoing training of various kinds have been only too ready to blame such symptoms on a reaction to the vaccine. As I mentioned earlier, such reactions appear to occur more frequently after the use of combined equine influenza/tetanus vaccines than with equine influenza vaccines alone.

The best advice at the moment appears to be that vaccination boosters should, whenever possible, be given before horses are turned out, or when they are at grass. If possible one should avoid vaccinating horses on their return from grass, when they are suddenly re-exposed to an environment made dusty by hay, straw, etc. If the vaccine manufacturer makes recommendations about resting the horse after vaccination, then these should be observed. Finally, horses with any sort of history of reaction to the vaccine should receive their influenza and tetanus vaccines on separate occasions.

Memories of the havoc caused by equine influenza epidemics have proved very short. A vociferous body of people who dislike any compulsion at all, have been only too ready to complain that compulsory equine influenza vaccination has made their horses ill and so should be discontinued. We have not had an outbreak of equine influenza in the UK since 1980 and it is perfectly reasonable to attribute this, at least in part, to the compulsory vaccination now required by so many shows, large and small.

A survey carried out during an epidemic in Newmarket in 1976 showed that as the percentage of vaccinated horses in a stable decreased, the incidence of the disease increased:

Percentage of horses in stable vaccinated	>75%	<75%	0%
Incidence of disease	7%	26%	65%

Other countries, where vaccination has not been encouraged so positively, have continued to suffer outbreaks. South Africa, for instance, had never had equine influenza and so had never practised any precautionary vaccination. When the virus did infect South African horses during 1986, it caused a disastrous epidemic. All forms of organised horse activities, such as racing and show jumping, came to a complete standstill for several months.

The majority of horse owners might well feel that an occasional reaction to the vaccine (however inconvenient) is a price worth paying for the common good. In any case the number of such 'reactions' is probably overstated by those who do not like compulsory vaccination. After all, one of the major vaccine manufacturers has recently disclosed that they have received only 23 reports of an adverse reaction to their vaccine over the past three years, despite possibly hundreds of thousands of doses used in that time. It has been suggested that the 'stress' of vaccination may cause horses which are carrying one of the equine herpes viruses to start releasing live viruses again and that these viruses cause the symptoms described. In the late 1970s the authorities in Sweden decided to make vaccination compulsory for all the trotting horses born in one year. Half the horses were given equine influenza vaccine and the rest were given a placebo. Naturally, neither owners, trainers or veterinary surgeons were told which horse had received which. Just as many 'side-effects' were reported in the horses given the placebo, or dummy vaccine, as in those given the real vaccine. Often it transpired that the symptoms were actually due to an infection with one of the other respiratory viruses. During the horses' racing careers it was found that vaccination did not affect the number of races a horse entered, its race time or the amount of prize money it won.

The other respiratory viruses

The virus whose effect is most commonly mistaken for equine influenza, or for the side-effects of equine influenza vaccination, is equine herpes virus (which used to be known as the rhinopneumonitis virus). The equine herpes virus type 1 (EHV1) has two distinct subtypes. Both subtype 1 and subtype 2 can cause respiratory problems but in the UK subtype 1 has traditionally been involved in outbreaks of contagious abortion rather than the purely respiratory symptoms associated with the subtype 2 virus. It has become accepted that the subtype 1 virus is the most active and that is why its effect in the body is great enough to affect the uterus and cause abortion. Since 1979 there have also been outbreaks of EHV1 subtype 1, which have been associated with varying degrees of paralysis of the hind legs. In such cases the virus affects the nervous system and is so virulent that taking virus from an affected horse and injecting it into another horse can cause nervous symptoms in that horse as well.

Although EHV1 subtype 1 can be a significant cause of respiratory disease in this country, abortion remains the major threat from this strain here. In the USA, however, EHV1 as a whole is considered a cause of abortion rather than of respiratory symptoms. It has been suggested that in America the infection is so common that horses receive repeated infections, and so build up sufficient immunity to limit any respiratory problems.

The respiratory symptoms of EHV1 are rather similar to those of equine influenza, although the temperature may not be so high. In both cases there can be a clear, watery discharge from the nose. The cough tends, however, to be more moist than in equine influenza. One of the problems with herpes viruses in all animals (including man) is that the infection can become latent. This means that the virus is not killed off by the body's defences but goes into a kind of hibernation. A horse with latent EHV1 is not infectious to other horses and does not produce antibodies against the virus, but it does have live viruses in its body. Stress factors of varying kinds (including breaking, stabling after a grazing period, hard training, racing and so on) can reactivate the virus and start it multiplying again.

There is a killed oil adjuvant vaccine for EHV1 subtype 1. This was developed to provide protection against contagious abortion in the USA. Initial clinical research in this country has failed to show any benefit from the use of the vaccine in reducing the incidence of respiratory disease. Recently, however, it has been suggested that the incidence of EHV1 abortion is increasing so much in this country that more use should be made of this vaccine. Natural immunity against EHV1 is comparatively short-lived. Not surprisingly, therefore, immunity after vaccination is also short-lived. Mares have to be vaccinated in the fifth, seventh and ninth months of pregnancy (or the equivalent in empty mares). The schedule has to be repeated every year.

There is a live attenuated EHV1 subtype 1 vaccine which is said to protect against the respiratory symptoms but not against the abortions. It requires two initial doses separated by four to eight weeks, with annual boosters. There have been doubts raised about the wisdom of using a live vaccine in these circumstances, not least because it might make diagnosis of the disease virus more difficult. There has not been any information presented yet about the vaccine's effect against the EHV1 subtype 2 virus, which is still responsible for most of the herpes respiratory disease in horses in Britain. Overall the effectiveness of EHV1 vaccination programmes has not been reliable enough to encourage official bodies to make their use compulsory, despite the economic cost of the disease. There is some evidence that vaccinating against just one strain may increase the horse's susceptibility to the other strain. So future commercial vaccines will probably need to include both strains in order to provide protection against the respiratory disease. Such a vaccine would be a significant improvement on those at present available. Research is continuing to find an effective combined equine influenza/EHV1 vaccine. Several apparently promising lines have been followed up but so far no such vaccine has reached the market, where a rich reward awaits a vaccine which would reduce so dramatically the number of coughing horses. Work on immune stimulating complex (ISCOM) vaccines, which utilise only fragments of the virus to stimulate immunity rather than the whole virus, may overcome these problems. Such vaccines certainly appear to stimulate much higher antibody levels than our present vaccines.

In America, equine viral arteritis (EVA) causes respiratory symptoms which are not unlike those caused by equine influenza or EHV1, i.e. there is a fever and a nasal discharge. Most cases, however, go on to develop raised areas of oedema (accumulated fluid under the skin). If pregnant mares become infected, they abort. At the present time this disease does not occur in the UK. When there was an outbreak of EVA in Kentucky

Table 4.1 The common symptoms of respiratory virus infections.

Symptom	Points to Note
Cough	Dry with equine influenza, moist with other viruses
Nasal discharge	Usually clear at first, becoming thicker
Fever	May have subsided before cough appears
Spreads rapidly	

during 1984 very strict precautions were instituted for the control of the importation of horses from America in order to ensure that the disease was not brought into this country. In America there is a vaccine available which appears to give good protection against the virus. Despite this, however, horses which have been vaccinated over there are not allowed to be imported into this country because of the difficulty in distinguishing EVA antibodies produced as a result of vaccination from those produced as a result of a natural infection.

The coughing horse

One of the reasons why horse owners become aware that their horse is suffering from even a mild respiratory infection is that the symptom most commonly produced, a cough, is so obvious. Owners may be unaware that their horse has a temperature of 104°F (40°C) (which is serious) but they will know that it 'coughed four times today' (which is probably not serious). People sometimes refer to 'the cough' as if it was an overall term covering all respiratory infections. They also tend to gauge whether a horse has recovered from an infection or not by whether it still coughs. This is not an accurate understanding of what goes on in the horse after a respiratory virus infection. Long after any actual virus particles have been killed by antibodies and cells in the blood, you may still find that the horse is coughing more than normal. It will not be infectious but may simply have some remaining inflammation in its pharynx (the cavity linking the larynx, oesophagus and mouth). This may take four to six weeks to die down, and during that time whenever the flow of cold air over the inflamed area increases, the increased irritation will cause coughing. This is one reason why after an infection horses will often continue to cough when they start exercise, even though they no longer cough in the stable. Another reason why horses continue to cough after the infection is killed off is that during the infection mucus becomes trapped in the alveoli, or air sacs, in the lung, and this mucus continues to cause irritation until it is removed one way or another.

Infections are not the only cause of increased mucus accumulation in a horse's lung. Irritation of the sensitive membranes lining the bronchioles and alveoli (Fig. 4.1) by dust particles will do so. When a horse breathes in air, any very large particles tend to become deposited as the air

Fig. 4.1 Electron micrograph of a respiratory membrane 'worn' almost smooth by dust, etc. Compare this with Fig. 4.2 which has a normal number of cilia. (*Courtesy of Boehringer Ingleheim Ltd.*)

passes over the turbinate bones in the nose. (These scroll-shaped bones stir up the air flow and warm it before the air passes down to the more sensitive parts of the respiratory system.) The further down the system the air passes, the smaller any particles have to be if they are to remain 'suspended' in the air that is travelling down the airways. A survey found that there might be ten times as many dust particles in the air in a stable during winter than there were outside in the open air. Around 40% of these particles were small enough to penetrate right down into the alveoli, compared with the 1% of the particles in the open air which were small enough to do so.

Down in the lung alveoli the fine dust particles which are still carried by the air come into almost intimate contact with the horse's blood-stream. It has to be that way to enable the oxygen of the air to be readily absorbed by the blood. Whereas the lungs welcome oxygen, however,

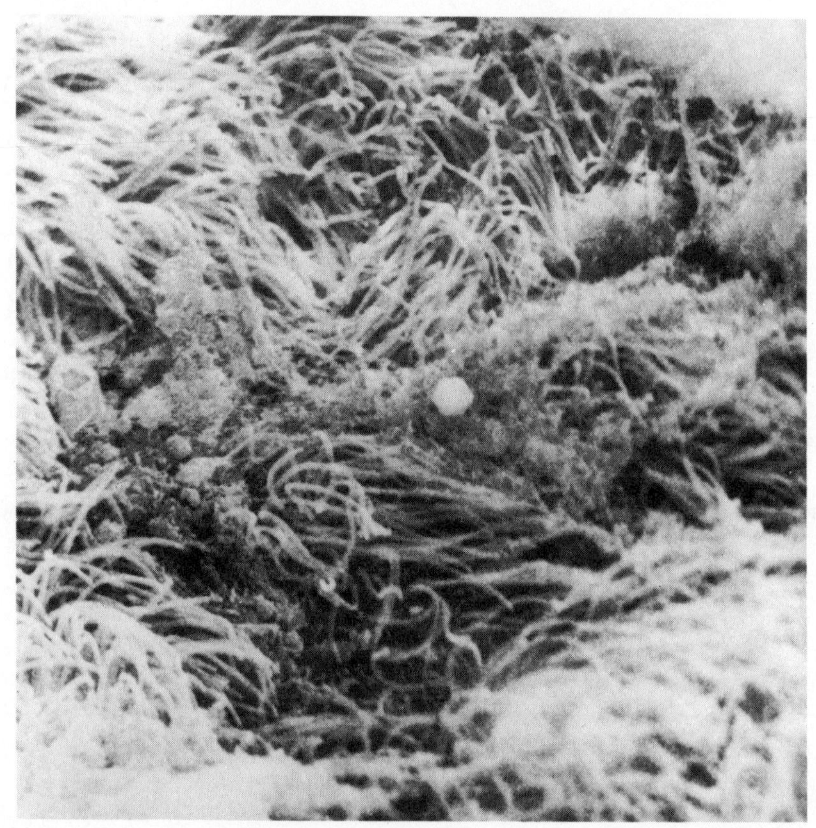

Fig. 4.2 Electron micrograph of the lining of the trachea, or windpipe. Notice the large numbers of cilia present and the single dust particle in the centre. (*Courtesy of Boehringer Ingleheim Ltd.*)

they do not welcome foreign bodies. The lungs can become inflamed and produce mucus to wash away the dust. The body has an 'escalator system' to remove this mucus from the lungs. The linings of the trachea, bronchi and bronchioles are covered with microscopic hairs called cilia (Fig. 4.2). These beat in a co-ordinated pattern (rather like the effect of a gust of wind blowing across a ripe corn field) and move the mucus on until it reaches the pharynx where most of it is swallowed. Only if relatively large amounts of this mucus are being produced will there be a nasal discharge as well as swallowing of the mucus. Some horses are particularly poor at clearing dust and mucus from the lungs. Of course coughing speeds up the clearing of mucus considerably. To some extent it is true that the faster air is forced through the airways, e.g. during a cough, the more mucus will be picked up as well. So coughing is not the undesirable action which so many horse owners think it is. If we have a coughing horse, our first thought should not be 'how can I get rid of that cough?', rather it should be 'what is causing that cough?'

I mentioned earlier that, as far as the lung alveoli were concerned, dust was a foreign substance. As has been stated the horse has a special immune system to cope with foreign bodies. In some cases the horse becomes increasingly sensitive to stable dust until it becomes allergic to it in varying degrees. This then produces the condition known as chronic obstructive pulmonary disease (COPD) or broken wind.

The problems of dust allergies

The dust particles most likely to trigger off this allergy are fungal spores, especially those of the *Micropolyspora Aspergillus* families. They are almost always present in hay and straw, even when these are of top quality. There may be as many as sixteen million spores in each breath that the horse takes in. Dust in general does not trigger off the allergy, only the particular foreign substance to which the horse is sensitive. Having said that, horses with COPD may be more sensitive to other irritants such as the dust from clipping horses or respiratory infections. These are not the underlying trigger factor, however, merely temporary irritants rather like sand getting into your eyes and making them close.

It is important to appreciate what happens down in the lungs themselves during COPD. Affected horses have more mast cells than normal in their lungs. These cells contain chemicals such as histamine which, if they are released, cause constriction of the tiny airways (broncho-constriction), increased production of mucus and general inflammation. The mast cells in a horse with COPD have cell walls which are more fragile than normal, and the mast cells easily break open and release the histamine into the lung tissue. The lungs of a COPD horse therefore show broncho-constriction, and increased production of thick, tenacious mucus. The result is that the airways are blocked for two reasons: by the broncho-constriction and by the thick mucus.

From the owner's point of view, there are a number of symptoms which might alert them to the fact that their horse has problems. It will tend to breathe more quickly than normal, even at rest. A resting respiratory rate of 20 or more breaths a minute in a horse which is not off its food and does not appear to have an infection may well point to COPD. The affected horses usually have a chronic cough as a result of trying (often unsuccessfully) to clear the thick mucus from their lungs. Some of the mucus is cleared from the lungs by the cilia, and so the horse may well also have a thick discharge from its nose. In some horses you will only notice the coughing and discharge after feeding or when the horse has had its head down grazing.

So far in my description of COPD there has been no indication of quite why this condition used to be called 'broken wind' or 'heaves'. Our knowledge of what is going on inside the lungs provides the clue to why this was. The drastically reduced airways mean that it takes much more physical effort to breathe in and out, especially out. In a normal horse, the elasticity of the lungs is sufficient to empty the lungs; the muscles of the thorax are only used to fill them. In a COPD horse the elasticity of the lungs is no longer sufficient to empty them, so the muscles must also be used to push the remaining air out. If we watch such a horse breathing out, we see the thorax shrink as the elasticity empties the lungs and then, after a brief pause, we see it shrink even further as the muscles expel the rest of the air. It is this break in what should be a smooth emptying of the lungs which gave rise to the name 'broken wind'. The extra muscular effort involved in breathing gave rise to the name 'heaves'. If a horse has had COPD for any great length of time, the muscles of the abdomen and the thorax which are involved in emptying the lungs become better developed than normal (in the same way that an athlete's muscles are developed by training) and their border can be clearly seen as a so-called 'heave line' (Fig. 4.3). Until relatively recently COPD was considered to be incurable because it was always thought to be associated with permanent damage to the lung. This damage, which is called emphysema, is the breakdown of the walls of the lung alveoli to give bigger air spaces which do not contribute to the transfer of oxygen from the atmosphere to the bloodstream (Fig. 4.4). We can understand how this happens; if the

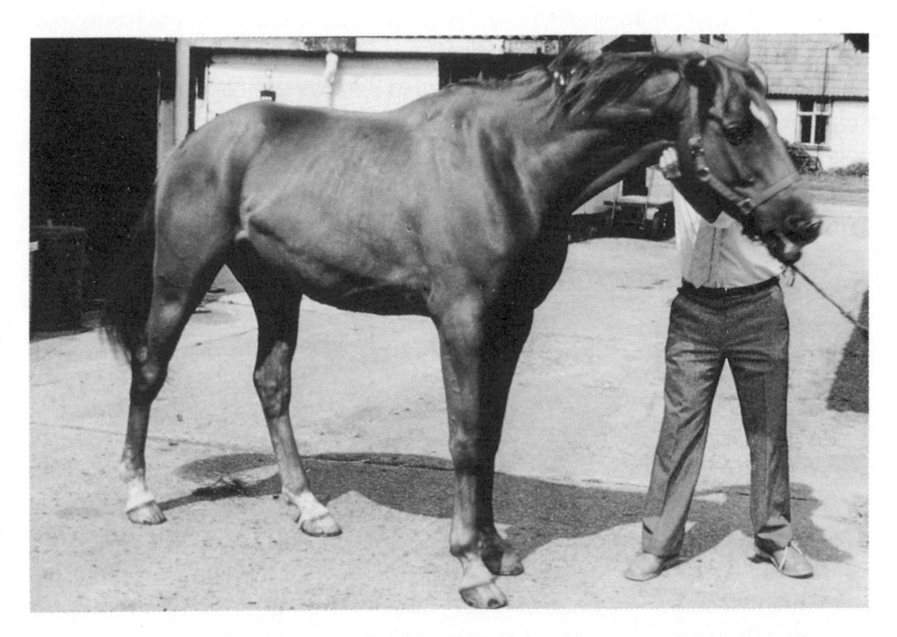

Fig. 4.3 A horse with a 'heave line'. (*Courtesy Boehringer Ingleheim Ltd.*)

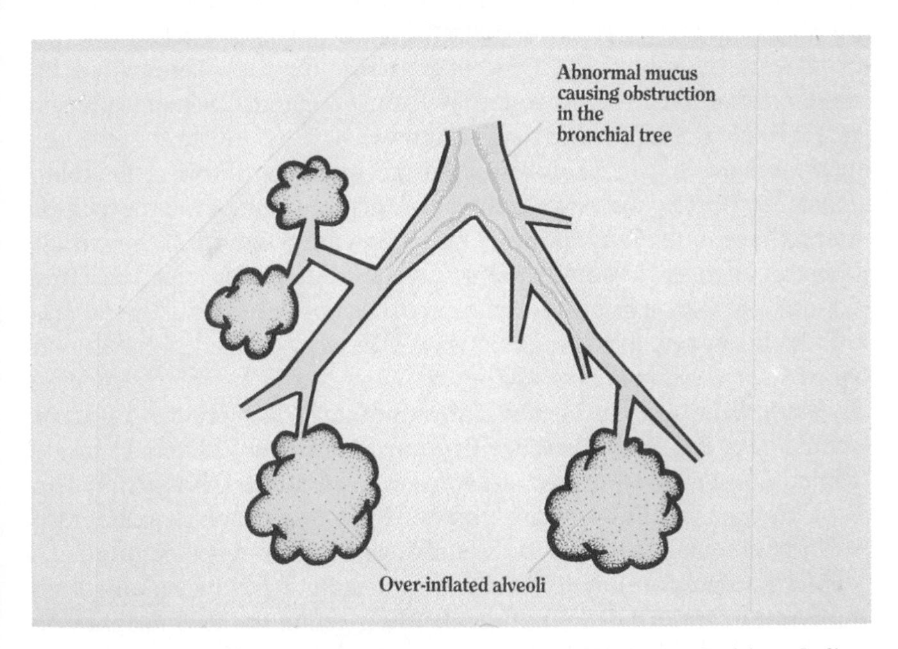

Fig. 4.4 Emphysema of the bronchioles. (*Courtesy of Boehringer Ingleheim Ltd.*)

airways are vitually blocked by mucus etc. they can act as a one-way valve. The powerful muscles of inspiration suck air in, the weakened expiratory system fails to empty the lungs completely, but when the horse breathes in again it still takes in its normal amount of air. As a result the alveoli become over-inflated and their walls rupture. How the impression became general that all broken-winded horses had significant emphysema seems difficult to understand because surveys of the lungs of horses with COPD which have died have failed to find emphysema in most of them. So although emphysema is a permanent change in the lungs, most horses with COPD do not have significant emphysema and so are not necessarily permanently affected.

A clean-air regime

The way to overcome COPD, and so prove that a horse is not necessarily permanently incapacitated as a result of the condition, is to institute a 'clean air regime'. We must do everything within our power to reduce the number of air particles to which the horse is hypersensitive. One way to do this is to avoid stabling altogether. Out in the paddock the horse will not come into contact with the fungal spores at all. There are a very small number of horses which are hypersensitive to pollen or grass, and which show worse symptoms of COPD at grass then they do when stabled, but these are the exception. In countries such as Australia, where horses are rarely stabled, COPD is virtually unknown.

If the horse has to be stabled, then we want that stable to be free of spores. So start by vacuum cleaning and then washing all the walls, floors and ceilings so that any spores lying around are removed. If there is any opening whereby 'contaminated' air can pass directly into the stable from adjoining stables, e.g. via a common roof space, then this must be blocked off. As far as possible the stable should be kept upwind of any hay or straw stacks so that spores will not be blown into the stable. Ventilation is obviously important. The top stable door must be kept open, and there should be as much ventilation with clean air as possible. Even during the winter COPD will pose more of a threat to an affected horse's life than cold air ever will. It has been suggested that the ventilation should be sufficient to change the air in the stable eight to ten times per hour.

Modern pre-fabricated stables are usually too low to allow for sufficient airspace and are noticeably stuffy even in winter. With a ridge roof stable, a height of about 12 feet to the ridge is not unreasonable and, in fact, needed to ensure a good airspace. Single plane roofs obviously should be higher.

Ventilation, however, can be improved without too much expense in most boxes. Ridge roof ventilators can be fitted to each box, as can gable end louvres. There should always be some means of creating a cross draught by having a window or simply a removable plank of wood or, again, a louvre on the side opposite the door as high up on the wall as possible. Only in strong wind conditions which create a noticeable draught inside the boxes should this be blocked up.

More use could also be made of mechanical extractors. Fans could be installed in each gable end of a row of boxes set to take out stale air and impurities. They don't need to be switched on all the time, of course, perhaps just when the air starts to become noticeably 'horsey'.

Surprisingly to some, the American barn system of stabling, with its long central aisle with usually open doors at each end, does not guarantee good ventilation as it is often found that the stale air pools in the boxes (box stalls) on either side. The individual stables still need their own ventilation facilities, as mentioned above, in many cases. Large complexes often need to be fitted with full artificial ventilation, and sometimes air conditioning systems. These complexes often experience severe dust problems when the stables are near, sometimes even overlooking, an indoor riding area, as the dust raised by the horses in even a well-watered surfaced arena is considerable. It would be much healthier for the horses (if inconvenient for their human attendants) if such boxes were 'turned around' by being closed off on the side facing the arena and having their doors facing away from it, preferably able to open directly outside, even if across a corridor.

Each yard will have its own practical and physical considerations as to the layout of its stabling, but, in arranging facilities, ventilation should receive much greater attention than is normally the case.

Horses with COPD should never be bedded on straw because the straw will be infected with fungi from the start. The most commonly used alternatives for bedding are wood shavings, peat and shredded paper. All these are almost certain to pose no risk at the start. If, however, you use a deep litter system whereby the bottom layers of bedding become hot and urine-soaked as it starts to decompose, then you will find fungi will start to invade the bedding. Rotting paper or shavings can be just as much a challenge to a horse with COPD as is straw. Whenever the bedding is disturbed, the numbers of dust particles are drastically increased. So ideally one should both muck out the stable and relay the bedding while the horse is out of the stable on exercise in order to allow as much time

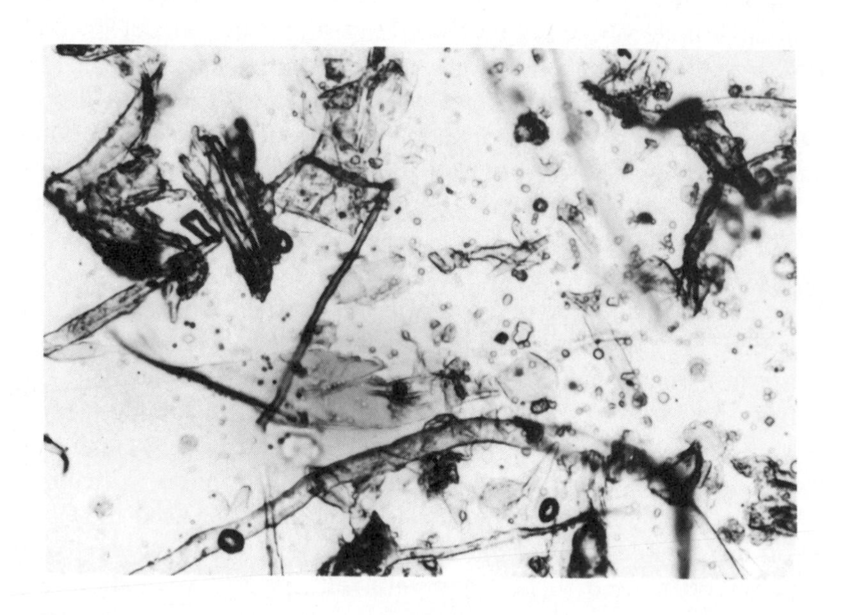

Fig. 4.5(a) A microscopic view of the dust from good hay. (*Courtesy Equigene Ltd.*)

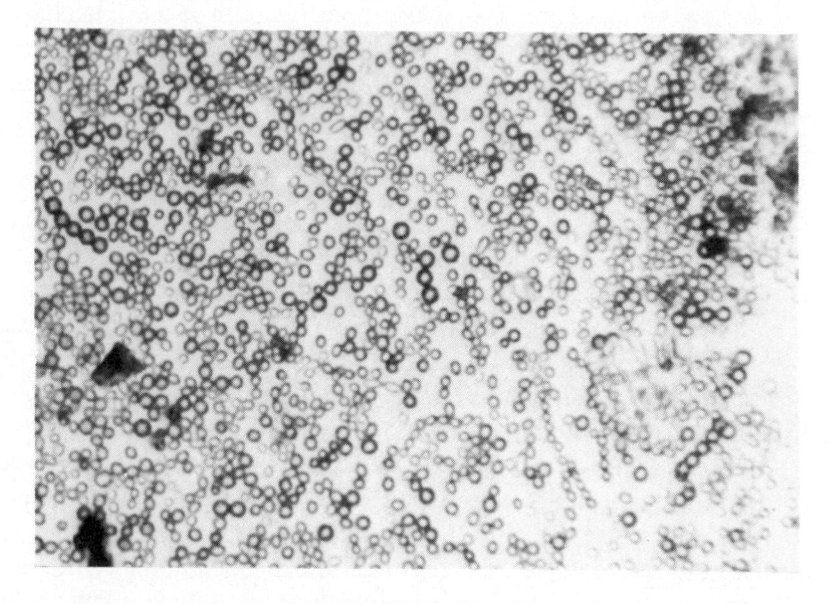

Fig. 4.5(b) A microscopic view of the dust from mouldy hay. Fungal spores obliterate almost everything else. (*Courtesy Equigene Ltd.*)

as possible for the particles stirred up in the air to settle.

The final management problem is the hay which the vast majority of stabled horses are fed to replace their natural grazing. Even the very best of hay will pose some danger (Fig. 4.5). Dusty, musty hay with obvious mould in it can be a disaster. It is not as if the spores are going to be diluted by the total volume of air in the stable. The horse literally buries its nose into the hay whilst it is eating it, and breathes in deeply the particles it stirs up. There are a number of solutions to this problem, of varying effectiveness.

(1) Feed the best hay you possibly can and store it in a really dry place. By best hay I do not mean the best in appearance, or the most expensive, but the hay with the fewest fungal spores. Using a machine called a slit sampler it is possible to suck a sample of the dust from hay onto a specially prepared microscope slide. This can then be examined to give an indication of the hay's quality from the respiratory point of view.
(2) Soak the hay before feeding. The operative word here is 'soak'. Merely pouring water over a haynet will only wash out a fraction of the dust which is present. Hay should be soaked for at least a couple of hours in a water container several times larger than the haynet. The water must be changed every day or so. You will see a thick scum of dust and hay particles collecting on the surface and there is no benefit in taking them out of one haynet and putting them into another one. Soaking hay washes away only a small percentage of the spores. It does help the spores to stick to the hay rather than being released into the air, but this effect is short-lived because the hay soon drys out. In any case, spores eaten on the hay may still trigger off some broncho-constriction.
(3) Horses can be fed silage instead of hay. If this is done, always feed the silage fresh straight from the clamp. Some people have found it more economical to use big bale silage. This is silage which is made in a large polythene bag, i.e. a mini silage clamp. This system is fine when everything goes right, but a number of horses have been killed as a result of being fed big bale silage which contains *Clostridium botulinum* toxin. If you want to feed big bale silage and be safe then check each bale for any perforation (however small) in the plastic wrapping. Discard any bag which has been punctured as the *Clostridium* may have gained entry to the silage. When you open a bale, discard any which have an unpleasant smell. Finally, check the acidity of the fluid draining from the bale using a pH meter. If it is significantly higher then 4.5, discard the bale. You

may well feel that it is easier and safer not to feed any silage made in this way.

(4) A form of imitation silage can be made in the stable yard at feeding time by placing the haynet in a thick polythene bag, pouring boiling water over it and sealing the bag as best you can for half an hour. It is doubtful whether this destroys significant numbers of fungal spores, but by softening the hay it may cause less irritation of the throat in horses which have a cough.

(5) There are products such as Propack which consist of grass vacuum-packed under pressure in a polythene bag within minutes of being harvested. This ferments, as does silage, but it is a completely different type of fermentation, i.e. a cold fermentation rather than a hot one. Propack is a very good foodstuff and is completely free of fungi when prepared. You do have to be careful, however, because such a desirable material will quickly become invaded by fungi. So only use one bag at a time, and don't leave it lying around. It should be stored as far away from hay and straw as possible, especially once opened. Bales where the polythene is damaged should not be accepted.

(6) In some ways the best solution to a hay-free diet is to feed complete horse nuts. These are nuts with a carefully balanced fibre content which are designed to be fed as the horse's sole food. In order to go some way towards mimicking the way a horse would pick at hay throughout the day, complete nuts have to be given in more frequent feeds than ordinary nuts. Some horses do experience problems of boredom when fed complete nuts because although one feeds more complete nuts in volume or weight than one does ordinary nuts, the complete nuts still take less time to eat than would a haynet. With the provision of 'toys' to interest the horse, or ensuring where possible that the horse can see plenty of activity going on from its stable, this can usually be overcome.

Clean air must be the most important step in treating and preventing COPD. It is no use paying lip service to the general principle and hoping that the details do not matter. Nor is it any use claiming that to follow the steps I have outlined would be expensive, and yet complaining when half measures fail to solve the problem. The clean air regime is not only of value in confirmed cases of COPD either. If a horse is coughing for any reason, even after infection with a virus, then the clean air regime will almost certainly be of benefit and will reduce the period of coughing.

Racehorse trainers have reported something called the loss of performance syndrome in horses after virus infections. These horses perform unexpectedly poorly at fast speeds and show excessive distress afterwards. Although the horses may well not cough or have a nasal discharge, we know from passing a special flexible tube called a fibreoptic endoscope down into the horse's trachea (Fig. 4.6) that there is thick mucus still being cleared from these horses' lungs. If it were possible to put all horses which appeared to have a respiratory infection on to a clean air regime straight away, we would probably markedly reduce the recovery period necessary afterwards.

Drugs and COPD

The provision of clean air is not the only thing we can do to help horses with COPD. It is possible to use drugs called bronchodilators to literally pull back open the constricted bronchioles. The most effective of these drugs in the horse is a drug called clenbuterol. This has the advantage of also slightly reducing the viscosity of the mucus down in the lungs (and so making it easier to remove it) and of increasing the activity of the cilia which, as I have explained, remove the mucus anyway. Dilation of the

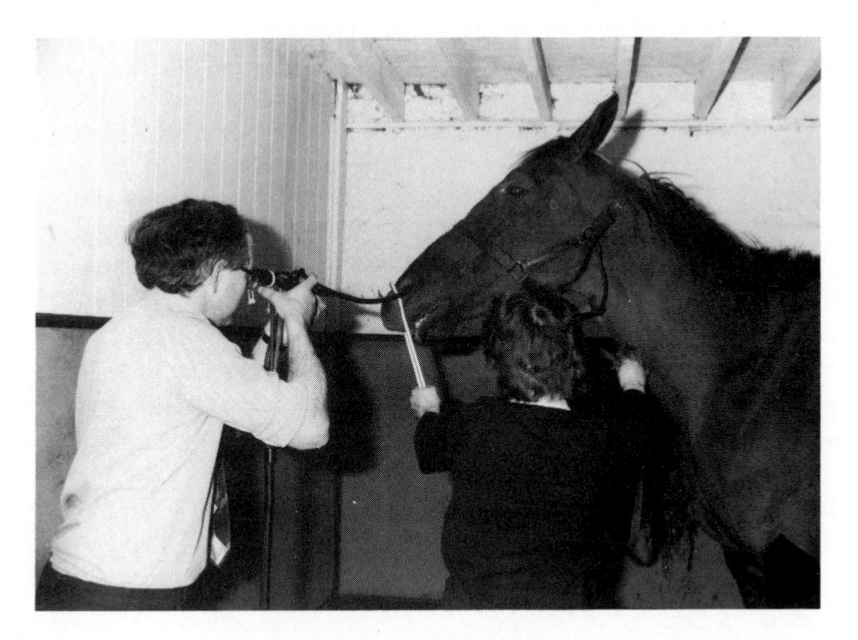

Fig. 4.6 Endoscopy of a horse.

airways allows more air down into the lungs and reduces the physical effort needed by the horse to get it there. It also loosens the attachment of any plugs of dry mucus which may have been blocking the airways. Of course, these effects are not achieved overnight. It has been suggested that one needs to treat a horse for one week for every month that it has been coughing prior to starting treatment.

Bronchodilators are basically treating an existing condition rather than preventing it, although it is possible (but expensive) to keep a horse on them continually. In some cases it is possible to prevent the bronchoconstriction and mucus production occurring in the first place. This is achieved by the use of a drug called sodium cromoglycate. This aims to stabilise the cell walls of the mast cells, so that they do not rupture and release histamine into the lung tissues. The stabilising effect may last for up to 20 days after a treatment. In order to work the drug has to come into direct contact with the mast cells. This is achieved, rather unusually, by using a nebuliser to produce a mist of fine droplets of the drug. The horse breathes this mist in through a special facemask. The whole system is powered by either a footpump or an electrical pump to force air through the nebuliser and associated tubes (Fig. 4.7). Sodium cromoglycate is a preventive measure rather than a treatment for existing problems. Giving it to horses already showing symptoms of COPD is rather like shutting the stable door after the horse has bolted. Once you have eliminated the symptoms by the use of clean air and bronchodilator drugs, then it may well be possible to use sodium cromoglycate to keep the horse symptom-free even in the presence of some hay or straw.

Unfortunately it is not possible to cure a horse with COPD from the point of view of the horse no longer being allergic. Even if you keep a horse trouble-free for a couple of years it will probably relapse at once if you relax your vigilance. That is not to say that you would notice any symptoms immediately. The horse can put up with reduced performance in a certain percentage of its lungs without any obvious effect. COPD tends to be a cumulative disease, with an increasing number of airways being constricted. That is why the symptoms often first show at the end of the stabling period, only to show earlier and earlier in that period in successive years. This is worth remembering when buying a horse. If the person selling it mentions that it has a bit of a cough at the end of last winter, but is perfectly all right now, then the alarm bells should start to ring. Very occasionally horses will become desensitised when the body decides there is just too much allergen around to make it worth even starting to respond to it, but so far efforts to produce this effect artificially have not been all that successful.

Fig. 4.7 Horse receiving treatment through a nebuliser. (*Courtesy Fisons Animal Health.*)

Recently some valuable information has come to light about how the long-term effects of respiratory viruses can mimic some of the effects of COPD and led to the rupture of blood vessels in the lungs after strenuous exercise. The resulting blood may become visible as a nosebleed, but in the majority of cases the owner remains blissfully ignorant that anything has happened because when the blood reaches the pharynx at the back of the mouth, it is swallowed. We now know that when the lungs are inflamed during a virus infection, the walls around the air sacs in the upper parts of the lungs become thickened. The number of blood vessels is increased, and it is bleeding from these vessels, as the lung tissue is stressed during forceful breathing, that we see. The thickening of the air sac walls I have referred to produces a similar effect to the constriction of the airways seen in COPD, and does appear to be a permanent and progressive effect. I cannot, therefore, stress strongly enough the

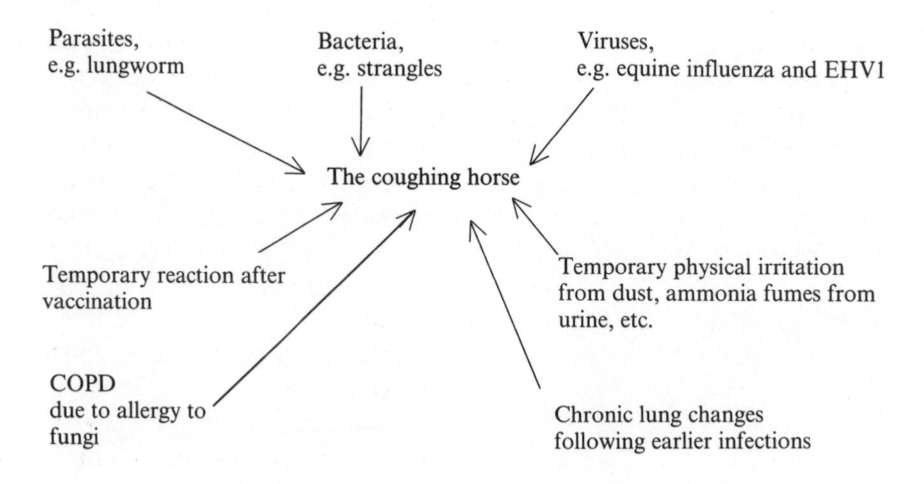

Fig. 4.8 The coughing horse.

importance of treating all respiratory virus infections seriously. The use of clenbuterol to keep the airways open and drugs called mucolytics to thin the mucus, in a young horse may be the only way to ensure that the horse still has some spare lung capacity available to cope with problems such as allergic obstructive disease in later life.

So the horse's vital respiratory system can come under attack from a whole variety of directions, with possibly disastrous results for the competition horse. It is worth remembering that in the wild, respiratory problems are not a serious threat. So if you want to avoid them, keep thinking back to the situation in the wild and model your stable management on that, i.e. keep your horse in the field and don't use a stable at all.

This is not so impractical as it may at first sound to those accustomed to keeping their horses, especially their working horses, stabled. As already mentioned, in Australia, and also New Zealand, stabling as a method of keeping horses is an exception rather than a rule. In parts of America, horses are rarely, if ever, stabled yet are hard, fit and hard-working. It seems to be mainly in overcrowded Europe that intensive stabling systems are most common. Indeed, in most parts of Scandinavia, at least Sweden and especially Norway, it can be quite rare to turn horses out because of the national shortage of land.

The problems are, even there, not insoluble, however. Here in Britain, there are various ways of keeping horses more naturally which do not receive the consideration they might when planning or changing stabling arrangements.

First of all, what are the other advantages of keeping horses more out than in, apart from the already-stated ones of the benefits to their respiratory health? They are able to do what nature intended and gently exercise themselves more or less all the time. It is in the horse's nature to wish to walk gently about grazing which they do, in the wild, for about 15 to 16 hours a day. Such gentle exercise makes repeated demands on the horse's physique and enables it to respond naturally to them by adapting and becoming stronger and fitter more gradually. The horse does, obviously, undertake of its own accord more strenuous exercise than walking, and horses so kept keep themselves half fit, particularly if corn-fed and in company, so saving their connections a good deal of the more mundane, slower work needed in getting and keeping a horse fit.

It also cannot be good for an animal intended to be more or less always on the move to receive its exercise in one bout of two hours out of the 24 and be left doing virtually nothing for the rest of the time, particularly when that one stint contains some quite stressful fast or physically demanding work.

A second advantage is the labour saved not only on reduced 'manual' exercise but on mucking out and bedding down stables. It is good hygiene to remove the horses' droppings wherever and however they are kept, but picking up droppings from a paddock or other enclosure involves on the whole less labour than actually mucking out and bedding down individual stables. There is also a financial saving on bedding and on stabling maintenance.

One of the main complaints about keeping competition horses largely at grass is that the grass intake interferes with the often minutely-planned diet of such horses, and that the grass will make the horses unduly fat and soft. With modern grass mixes and knowledge of seeds, it is perfectly possible for a knowledgeable seed company, agronomist or equine nutritionist, or suitably interested veterinary surgeon, to formulate a suitable grass mix which will result in a sward low in undesirable nutrients, and appropriate for athletically working horses. Grass, in any case, is obviously the horse's natural food and hydroponic grass now plays a significant part in the diet of many such horses, not least those in our 1988 Olympic team, so the objections against grass *per se* are unfounded. The right mix is all that is needed. Poorish quality (i.e. low feeding value) grazing, but clean and well managed, is what should be aimed at – something like the grass used for grazing sheep rather than dairy cattle. Many successful endurance horses are kept in this way.

In winter, better shelter facilities than normal could be provided, plus the modern super-warm, lightweight and comfortable New Zealand rugs.

At any time of year, horses will thrive better with amenable companions, even one small pony, than alone, of course this being again their natural lifestyle. A horse alone in a field or other enclosure may spend a good deal of its time moping by the gate, not a very desirable pastime.

In areas where actual pasture is unavailable, or ground conditions prohibit turning out into a conventional field, other facilities for liberty can and should be provided to prevent the horse having to be stabled.

Establishments having existing outdoor, or even indoor, riding arenas could make at least partial use of them for accommodating horses when they are not needed for other purposes, provided the surfaces are kept well watered and not, therefore, likely to cause respiratory problems brought on by the mechanical irritant of dust. Obviously outdoor arenas are better from this point of view.

Yarding could certainly be made more use of in Britain. In this system, horses, or even just one horse, are kept in a surfaced, fenced area, usually with access to a covered area, a run-in shed or direct to the stable. When constructing yarding accommodation, it may, depending on the natural drainage of the area selected, be necessary to excavate down (as for an outdoor riding manège), infilling with a layer of coarse rubble, then finer stones and finally the surfacing material chosen, maybe on top of a third layer of finer material such as smooth gravel. Many yards, however, consist simply of earth. It does all depend on drainage as one of the advantages of yarding horses, apart from allowing them more access to fresh air, is to keep them away from excessively muddy conditions.

Yards like this can, if required, be entirely covered, with or without access to an outdoor area, maybe pasture. The system gives great scope for flexibility in the actual accommodation offered and also its size. Even a small area only the size of the stable itself opening directly off it gives the horse the chance to be outdoors when it wishes. Bull boxes with their attached pens, often in front of the actual box, are excellent for providing this type of accommodation, although the boxes themselves usually need the roofs raising if they are to accommodate horses.

The surfacing material should be chosen with some care. It must drain well, be safe for the horses, deep enough to prevent injury on a possibly hard ground surface underneath and not be unduly expensive for most people. It must not become deep and holding when rained on, nor scatter easily, nor, obviously, cause health problems.

Probably the best surfaces available for this purpose at the time of writing are wood chips as sold for outdoor riding arenas. Various surfaces are being tried with a view to providing all-weather racing tracks but these would appear to be too expensive for the purposes under consideration here. A good mixture, tried and proved in practice, is equal parts by weight of sand, salt and wood chips. It is tempting to top up the yard, when needed, by using up old shavings taken from boxes during mucking out, but this often results in dusty, deep going as they rot down.

Old fashioned straw yards would not, of course, be suitable for horses with respiratory problems, for which we are considering alternatives to stabling here. The dust and spores present in even good samples are kicked up into the air every time the horses move and more or less defeat our object of providing them with a clean-air environment.

The open stabling system, common on the continent, where horses are kept partly out and partly in large barns together rather than in individual stables can be beneficial provided the barns are not overstocked and, again, straw is avoided, care being taken to use a dust-free flooring material. In America and Australia, it is common to corral horses in a dirt enclosure with high, railed fencing, although the system has severe disadvantages in that no shelter is normally provided.

With a little imagination, it is possible to provide horses with accommodation which will keep them handy, content, reasonably clean and enable their diet to be controlled, without subjecting them to the artificial and often detrimental environment of a stable.

5 Feeding for health

The horse's digestive system

Man may have changed the appearance of the horse since domestication, inasmuch as we now have a wide variety of breeds, but one thing which he has not changed is the horse's digestive tract. This is still the same odd mixture of systems which the horse has had to cope with since it evolved on the prehistoric plains. In a peculiar way, horse owners seem to recognise this. When a horse has dental problems or colic, time and time again the owner asks 'what would have happened in the wild?' Yet they do not seem to make the same connection when any other body system goes wrong. In most cases, incidentally, the answer to the question is that the horse would die. The horse must eat and digest its food properly if it is to live.

Before considering what a horse should eat, it is important to have an overall view of its unique digestive system. As far as the mouth, oesophagus, stomach and small intestine are concerned, it is very like our own. The stomach is relatively smaller than ours because, like so many meat eaters, we are adapted so that we can accommodate a large meal when the hunting has been good. The horse, on the other hand, is a grazing animal and so only has to cope with small quantities of food at a time. At the end of the small intestine comes the first major difference between us and the horse; the horse has a large caecum, whereas ours is so small as to be almost non-existent. The less medically minded might not know that they have a caecum at all, because in people it is often referred to as the appendix. The other major anatomical difference between the horse's alimentary tract and that of a human being is that the horse has a very long and wide large colon compared with our own. This is because the horse had to be able to digest the cellulose which makes up so much of the bulk of plant tissue. Cellulose is not digested by ordinary digestive enzymes, and the horse has to provide a place where millions of bacteria can do the job. So the horse's large colon is equivalent to the cow's rumen. Both contain independent bacteria which work both for their own good and the good of the host animal.

The whole purpose of this book is to help the horse owner to avoid problems. To this end the question is often asked 'what should I feed my horse?' Practically all the common feedstuffs have advantages and disadvantages. We must start off by stating that the horse's natural food is grass. So, if possible, grass is what you should give your horse to eat.

The teeth

The horse bites the grass off with its front, incisor, teeth. It then gives it a quick crushing with its cheek, or molar, teeth before swallowing it. If a horse is parrot-mouthed, i.e. its upper incisor teeth make no contact with the bottom ones when it closes its mouth, then it will not be able to graze properly. It does not seem to matter if the horse is slightly parrot-mouthed; as long as there is some degree of contact between the jaws it will be able to manage. So if you are buying a horse it will depend on whether it is going to be continually fed concentrate foods or is going to graze as to whether the fact that the horse is parrot-mouthed is important.

The wild horse survives the winter by eating dried tussocks of old grass. Man has replaced this with hay. But the horse does not graze hay; it comes ready cut, in long lengths. So the incisor teeth are less important to the domestic horse. The molar teeth, on the other hand, are more important because this drier, more fibrous, material has to be broken up by chewing. Because of the way a horse moves its jaws during chewing, the actual grinding surfaces of the molar teeth wear at an angle. The bottom teeth are shorter along the outside of the jaw than they are on the inside of it. The upper molar teeth are obviously the other way around, i.e. longer on the outside (Fig. 5.1). Continual grinding can develop really sharp points at the edges of the grinding surface. So sharp points can develop on the outside of the upper molars and the inside edge of the lower molars.

Sharp edges on these teeth all too readily cause sore places and even ulcers on the sensitive lining of the cheeks or the tongue. If it hurts the horse to chew, then it will not chew more than is absolutely necessary. It is obvious that if your horse's teeth become very sharp, it might stop

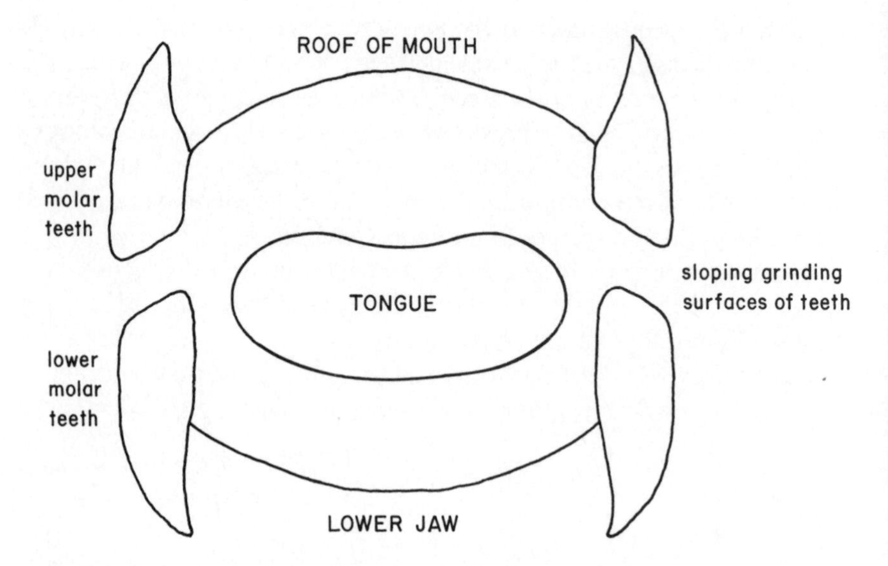

Fig. 5.1 Tooth wear: cross-section of the mouth showing tongue and teeth on either side.

eating altogether, or may keep picking food up and letting it fall out of its mouth again rather than chew it properly. Such a horse will rapidly lose weight and may die of starvation.

What horse owners all too often fail to realise, however, is that even a slight discouragement from chewing will reduce the horse's overall digestive efficiency. So do not wait until your horse cannot eat at all. Have its teeth checked regularly for the development of any sharp points. How often this needs to be done will depend on the individual horse. I have known a horse which could develop really sharp points within six weeks, whereas others may not do so even over a couple of years of chewing. I would suggest that you have your horse's teeth checked at least once a year. To examine them properly, it is necessary to use a device called a gag to hold the jaws well and truly open so that the veterinary surgeon can feel every single tooth without losing his or her fingers (Fig. 5.2).

If sharp points or other abnormalities do develop, it is relatively easy to restore your horse's chewing efficiency by rasping (or filing) them smooth. This does not hurt the horse because it does not have nerves extending right up the centre of its teeth in the way that human beings do.

Bacteria in the large colon

As mentioned earlier, the grass or hay will ultimately end up in the large

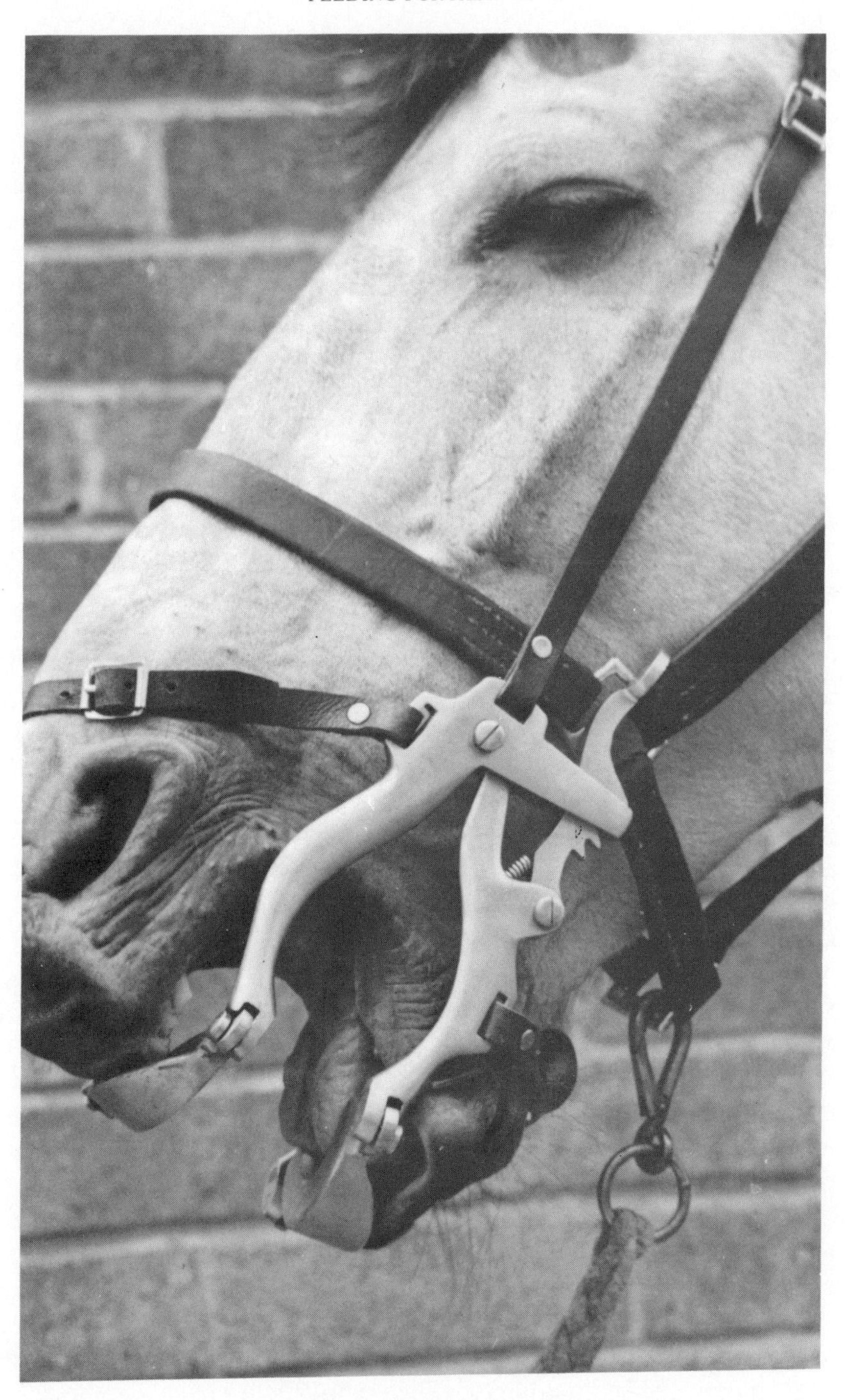

Fig. 5.2 Tooth gag in place.

colon where its fibre will be digested by the natural bacteria which live there, inside the horse and yet independent of it. Grass and hay are obviously completely different in texture and fibre content. The bacteria which digest grass best will be different from those which digest hay best. In fact it goes further than that because the bacteria which digest your hay best may be different from those which digest your neighbour's hay best. When a horse is on a settled diet, the bacteria in its large colon adapt themselves so that the most efficient blend is present. If you change your horse's diet suddenly, a proportion of the fibre will not be digested because there just will not be the right bacteria present in the large colon.

Impactions of the intestines, or blockages

If this happens a potential source of nutrients will have been wasted. It will also mean that the contents of the large colon will be more fibrous than normal. Perhaps this would not matter if the horse's large colon was a straight tube with a constant diameter bore. Unfortunately this is not the case. The horse's large colon is formed into two U-shaped loops, and where they join together the colon makes a 180° turn on itself so that the two loops lie on top of each other. If the fibre content of the food material is too great, it will not easily pass around this turn and may become impacted there. Two other factors make the situation even worse. Firstly the horse's body absorbs quite large amounts of fluid out of the large colon (it has, for example, to reabsorb the water part of the saliva and digestive juices used higher up the system). When the speed of flow around the bend (which is called the pelvic flexure) is slowed, even more fluid can be absorbed and so the contents become even drier and more fibrous. To exacerbate the problem, the diameter of the large colon almost halves as it makes that 180° bend.

If for any reason fibrous food is improperly digested, then the pelvic flexure is often the area where everything finally grinds to a halt. Such an impaction (and impactions can occur at other sites along the alimentary tract) will cause colic. The term colic, by the way, means nothing more than abdominal pain. There are various ways in which we will be able to tell that a horse has colic. If a horse has an impaction it obviously stops passing any droppings, although often not for some time after the impaction occurs because the droppings which have already passed the affected area will not be stopped. The horse becomes very lethargic, even dozy. It may kick at its stomach, which is one of the classic symptoms of colic. It is more likely to lie flat out on its side than it is to roll on the ground (the other classic symptom of colic).

The way to prevent your horse having an impaction is to avoid sudden changes in its diet, even of such staple items as hay or grass. It is possible for a horse to become impacted when it is turned out to grass suddenly, just as it is when the horse is suddenly stabled with hay. Care also needs to be taken during exceptionally cold weather because the frozen food may not be chewed and digested properly. Whilst on the question of uniformity of diet, it is worth pointing out that the horse very much appreciates regular meals, so that it can organise the bowel movements and the release of the digestive enzymes. Two meals a day at the same time of day will yield more nutritional value than either one meal giving the same weight of food, or than two meals a day fed at irregular times.

Grass and hay

One of the difficulties of hay is that its nutritional quality can vary tremendously. The quality of production and storage of hay is almost more important than the choice of plants in the original grass. If you are making your own hay, it may be possible to make decisions which will materially alter the hay's effect on your horse. Legume hays, for example, are more likely to become dusty or mouldy than grass hay. So if your horse has any respiratory problems, you would not want to make alfalfa, legume or clover hay. Plants tend to yield the greatest amount of energy at a different stage of growth than that at which they give the highest protein level, so resist the temptation to make hay as late as possible just in order to obtain the maximum weight yield. For most plants, hay is best made during the early stages of flowering.

We frequently talk of high protein concentrate feeds, even though their protein levels are only 12–15 %. Grass can, amazingly, give protein levels of 20 %. These percentages are, of course, on a dry matter basis. So the protein levels when grass and concentrates are compared by volume or just by weight will be different. The higher the grasses' leaf content, the greater its digestibility. This is especially important because high digestibility is linked to high protein quality.

'Hard' feed

The most popular food for horses after hay is probably oats although corn (maize) is widely fed in the USA. It should be pointed out straight away that good quality hay will supply all a mature horse's nutritional requirements if it is leading a 'natural' life. So if your horse is not carrying out any work, it will not need any oats. On the other hand, if the horse is regularly ridden or driven, then some supplementary food will be necessary. Such 'hard' feed must never be considered as the sole ration: it is a supplement to grass or hay. Oats may be being fed in order to boost the energy value of the diet of a working horse but they will also provide some fibre and protein for maintenance just as the hay will provide some energy for exercise.

Oats

Oats have the lowest weight per volume of all the cereals. In other words, a pound of oats will occupy more space than a pound of barley. You can see at once the futility of feeding 'by the scoop'. A scoop of oats is not nutritionally equivalent to a scoop of any other cereal. Your scoop of oats may not even be equivalent to your neighbour's scoop because oats can vary in quality tremendously. As oats are used less and less for other purposes, there may be less choice, in the UK at any rate. Their quality is unlikely, therefore, to rise. Old grooms often bemoan the fact that our oats are nowhere near as good as they used to be.

Oats also have the lowest concentration of digestible energy of the common cereals. They are in many ways the safest cereal to use as hard feed because whether you alter the amount of oats you feed by volume or by weight, you will have to make a relatively great percentage change before you significantly alter the nutritional value. Some owners refer to a food as being hotter than another or to it making their horse hot (by which they mean lively and difficult to control). This is because they fail to appreciate the basic nutritional principle that feeds have different values when compared by weight, by volume and by their nutritional yield. If you feed the equivalent energy value of two feeds (whether that means you are feeding dissimilar weight and volume or not) then the feeds will have the same effect, i.e. neither will make the horse 'hotter' than the other.

Maize

This is the corn of cornflakes. It is usually fed cooked and flaked to horses. Maize can provide up to 50% more energy than oats from the same weight of grain. So greater care has to be taken in using it to feed horses because even slight alterations in the amounts you feed will have a more marked effect on the horse's diet. On the other hand it is not as good a source of protein as oats are, and contains very little fibre.

Barley

You must not feed barley as straight grain. Apart from other considerations, it ferments readily (as lovers of beer and whisky will know) and will do so in the horse's digestive system. So barley should be rolled or crimped before being fed to horses. Steam flaking has the same effect as rolling or crimping and, despite some advertising claims, does not have any effect on the amount of 'heat' it causes to be produced.

Bran

Anyone who has tried to slim will know that wheat bran has a very high fibre content. It is actually the husk covering of the grain and is usually considered to have very little nutritional value. One reason for this is that bran is very bulky, so the horse find it difficult to eat enough bran to provide a worthwhile amount of energy. This bulk gives bran a laxative effect and bran mashes are often fed purely for this purpose. In days gone by, horses were usually given a mash once a week on their rest day. All too often the new modern horse owner does not give his horse a rest day, and may not even know what a mash is. So I make no apologies for mentioning that a bran mash is made by pouring boiling water over the bran until it is stirred into a stiff type of porridge. It is then left to cool to a safe temperature for the horse to eat. (A bran poultice is made the same way, but that is another story.) Bran mashes are very useful when a horse suddenly has to have its exercise programme reduced. They speed up the passage of the remaining high energy food, whilst still providing the bulk to which the digestive system is accustomed.

It is not a good idea to feed too much bran to young, growing horses. Bran contains more than ten times as much phosphorus as it does calcium, and the calcium which is present does not seem to be absorbed by the horse. The ideal ratio of calcium to phosphorus in the diet is 1.1:1, so feeding large quantities of bran can result in the horse getting far too much phosphorus. In the mature horse this may not matter in the short term, but in a young horse which is still making bone it is important because it will upset the calcium and phosphorus levels in the bone which is still being made.

Sugar-beet pulp

When it is available this can be a very valuable feedstuff. It can, for example, provide almost as much energy per weight of feed as oats. It has one very important drawback as a feedstuff, however. It has a high dry matter content in the form in which it is supplied, and as soon as it comes into contact with any moisture it swells enormously. If you feed the pulp just as it is, then it will swell up as soon as it becomes mixed with saliva. This often leads to the swelling pulp becoming stuck in the horse's oesophagus. The horse is then said to be 'choked', and it becomes very distressed. Large amounts of frothy saliva collect in the horse's oesophagus above the blockage, and this may seriously interfere with the horse's breathing. Without treatment a choked horse will certainly die. Even if the pulp does not block the oesophagus, it will certainly swell up in the stomach, and may even cause the rupture of this relatively small organ.

Treatment of a choked horse consists of passing a stomach tube down to the obstruction and sucking out the pulp little by little. Prevention is obviously vitally important if you are going to use this particular feedstuff. The pulp must be soaked in water for at least 12 hours before being fed to a horse. If you are using pulp which has been made into nuts or pellets, then they should be soaked for 24 hours. This ensures that no further swelling will take place inside your horse. As a result of this soaking, the nutritional value of the pulp (when measured either by volume or by weight) is decreased.

Compound feeds

In some respects, proprietary horse feeds are the most misused of all feedstuffs. The manufacturer spends a considerable amount of time, money and effort in developing a balanced feed, i.e. one which provides all the energy, protein, vitamins and minerals that the horse will require. The horse owner pays the manufacturer for his efforts, and all too often promptly goes and ruins them by adding extra ingredients. So if a horse cube contains the correct amount of calcium and phosphorus to balance that available in an average sample of hay, adding extra bran unbalances it immediately. There are two particular respects in which the average horse owner considers he knows better than the nutritionist: energy and vitamins. If the owner considers that their horse needs more fuel for energy, then all too often instead of feeding more of the compound feed (and thus preserving the balance) they feed extra oats or some other grain. Similarly with vitamins (as I will discuss later) there is a great desire to add a vitamin supplement to the diet. If you are using a proprietary horse feed, then before you put anything extra into your horse's manger you should ask yourself the question: 'Is my nutritional and other expertise such that I really do know better than the person who devised this feed?' I suspect that only on rare occasions will the honest answer be 'Yes'.

Another way in which proprietary foods are misused is that horse owners tend to lump them all together, without realising that many manufacturers make specific feeds for performance horses, breeding mares or even for ponies which will be spending much of their time out in the field (Table 5.1). Although I doubt whether the average horse owner is sufficiently well informed to know better than the feed companies how to balance a diet, he should know when to change from one ration to another for maximum effect at the most economic cost. For example, if your horse is recovering from an injury or illness, then a stud ration is more likely to meet its requirements for a high protein/low energy diet than a racehorse ration. At present nobody makes a ration specifically for the convalescent horse.

In recent years the amount of coarse feeds sold for horses in the UK has increased dramatically. Horse owners like to be able to see what their horse is getting, and to know that it isn't just 'the sweepings off the floor' which have been compacted into nuts. Because they use molasses as a binding agent, these coarse feeds are not as dusty as some nuts can be, which is an advantage if the horse has respiratory problems. Loose feeds

Table 5.1 Analysis of different types of concentrate feed.

Ration	Crude protein	Fibre	Oil	Ash	Digestible energy in MJ/kg
Horse and pony cubes	10.5%	14.0%	2.5%	10.3%	10.1
Event cubes	10.5%	14.5%	2.5%	9.5%	10.7
Racehorse cubes	14.0%	9.5%	3.25%	7.5%	13.4
Stud cubes	16.0%	7.5%	4.25%	8.5%	13.6
All fed with hay					
Complete nuts fed without hay but in greater quantities	10.0%	20.0%	2.5%	8.5%	9.6
Coarse mix	11.0%	8.5%	3.0%	—	12.6

also take longer to eat than pelletted feeds. This reduces boredom and may help digestion.

Vitamins

Most people tend to think of vitamins as substances which have to be present, albeit in minute amounts, in food to sustain life. This was certainly the thinking about vitamins in man when they were first discovered and evaluated. In horses and many other animals this is not the case. Vitamins remain substances which are vital in very small amounts to sustain life, but they may not need to be present in the horse's food. In a number of cases the horse's own organs can synthesise the vitamin in question. In other cases, it is the bacteria within the alimentary tract which manufacture the vitamin, and this is then absorbed in the same way as if it had been in the feed.

Vitamin A is important to your horse's health. The horse makes its vitamin A from a substance called carotene, and in view of this it might be no surprise that vitamin A is important for vision. The myth that eating carrots helped one to see better at night is still common, nearly 50 years after it was coined in World War II. Vitamin A is also important for bone growth and in the epithelial cells which cover the body and line the gut, lungs and so on.

Green feeds such as grass contain good levels of vitamin A. Unfortunately, though, most of the vitamin is destroyed when grass is dried to make hay. So if your horse is not grazing regularly, then it will need extra vitamin A. I must remind you again, though, that compound feeds may well have a vitamin supplement which will compensate for this.

There are several types of vitamin B. Sometimes they are identified by number, e.g. vitamin B_1, and sometimes by name, in this case thiamine. As thiamine is present in both grass and cereals, horses do not often suffer from a deficiency. High levels of energy production rely on the presence of thiamine for the removal of lactic acid from the working muscles. If the acid is not efficiently removed, it will damage the muscle fibres like any other acid. So if your horse is undergoing really strenuous exercise, there may be some point in giving extra thiamine.

Vitamine B_{12} is perhaps the best known vitamin of all. It has acquired a reputation as a wonder substance which is solely responsible for healthy red blood cells. Consequently many horse owners expect to be able to increase the number of their horse's blood cells overnight just by a dose of vitamin B_{12}. This reputation is quite unjustified. It is certainly true that vitamin B_{12} is a vital part of the haemoglobin mechanism which enables red blood cells to carry oxygen around the body. It is not possible, however, for a horse to become deficient in vitamin B_{12}.

The reason for this is that the bacteria in the horse's colon produce such large amounts of vitamin B_{12}, that even if the horse does not receive any in its food it will absorb more than it needs from the colon. Injections or tonics of vitamin B_{12} perform no function for the horse, therefore, although they may make the owner feel as though he is doing something. Even on those occasions (again much rarer than owners imagine) when a horse is anaemic, feeding extra vitamin B_{12} will not speed up the production of red blood cells one little bit.

Vitamin C is the scurvy vitamin, or rather it is the vitamin whose lack used to cause scurvy in early sailors. Otherwise known as ascorbic acid, it can be manufactured by the horse's body. There is some evidence, however, that stress can lower the levels of ascorbic acid which circulate around the bloodstream. This in turn can lead to reduced resistance to viruses. It is hard to give extra vitamin C because it is unstable in pellets or horse cubes. Giving relatively large amounts (⅔ oz/20 g per day) of the pure substance by mouth will, however, raise the blood levels.

Vitamin D is, of course, the vitamin which is associated with bones, and as such is especially important in young growing horses. If they do not obtain enough of the vitamin, they develop rickets. Their bones then become relatively soft, painful and deformed. Vitamin D is unusual because the horse can also have too much of a good thing. Indeed there are several poisonous plants in various parts of the world which are dangerous precisely because of their vitamin D activity. This vitamin is also unusual because there are much higher levels in dried hay than in fresh grass (whereas with most vitamins it is the other way around). The horse is not dependent on hay for its vitamin D supplies, however, because it can manufacture it in the skin.

Vitamin E always seems to be linked with the mineral selenium. It is considered to be necessary for efficient muscle function and maximum reproductive efficiency. It would appear that even racehorses do not need extra vitamin E for normal muscle activity, but there is still some doubt over whether giving extra vitamin E will help in the prevention and treatment of azoturia. Beware of the fact that vitamin E is relatively unstable and so old feedstuffs and vitamin supplements may not have their advertised levels. It is perhaps worth pointing out at this juncture that vitamin supplements should have a stated expiry date. Always make sure that they are used up well within that limit, and do not bother buying them in the first place if they do not have a stated expiry date.

Minerals

Just as some horse owners expect to be able to increase the number of red blood cells which their horse has by giving extra vitamin B_{12}, so some expect to achieve the same effect by giving their horse extra iron. Iron is certainly an integral part of the haemoglobin, which actually transports the oxygen in the blood. Deficiency of iron is only one of many possible causes of a horse being short of red blood cells, however. Other factors, such as the health of the whole blood manufacturing system or the rate at which blood is being lost, e.g. as a result of internal bleeding, are far more important. The reason why iron supplements are not needed is that the horse has an extremely efficient recovery system which prevents it losing any of the iron which it already has. So very little iron, for example, is passed out in the faeces. In addition, iron is a plentiful mineral in feeds, soil, etc. Feeding extra iron has never been proved to add a single gram of haemoglobin to a horse's blood.

Calcium and phosphorus, on the other hand, are minerals which may well need supplementing in a horse's diet at certain stages of its life. It is customary to deal with the two minerals together because they are often found together in the body. Practically all the calcium and more than 80% of the phosphorus in a horse's body are a compound called hydroxyapatite, which makes up part of the bone structure (in the ratio of two parts of calcium to one part of phosphorus).

The amount of calcium which a horse can absorb from its diet will be affected by the levels of other minerals, such as phosphorus or magnesium which are present. It will also be affected by the levels of other feedstuffs, such as proteins, carbohydrates and fats. Contrary to what one might expect, feeding high levels of calcium will not have any effect on the levels of calcium in the horse's blood. This is because the skeleton acts as a reservoir, holding back calcium and keeping blood calcium levels constant in the same way as a dam might keep the water levels of a river constant. The skeleton does this in a rather clever way. In normal circumstances a horse's bones are constantly forming new hydroxyapatite crystals of bone here and breaking down crystals there. This is the case even in adult horses, although their rate of activity will be lower than in growing horses. If the blood calcium levels drop below a critical level, the horse will make less new bone and the continuing breakdown of other crystals will raise the blood calcium level.

It does not take the brains of an Einstein to realise that if such a process continues for any length of time, the horse's bones will have fewer bone crystals present than they ought to have. In other words, the bone will be softer, or less dense. A young growing horse in such a situation will continue to grow in size, but the soft skeleton will be liable to problems. Calcium and phosphorus can be fed to horses in the correct proportions by using ground bone-meal. Giving 5–6 oz (140–170 g) daily would provide all a growing horse's requirements and be much cheaper than a proprietary mineral supplement. In practice, of course, smaller quantities are fed because you are only 'supplementing' other food.

Sodium is another mineral which can often be fed to your horse far more cheaply than as a proprietary supplement. Some mineral supplements contain a very high proportion of salt, although you would not think so by looking at their cost. If your horse is working very hard, so that it is sweating noticeably, then it will be losing considerable amounts of sodium. It may well therefore need extra sodium in addition to that provided by a balanced diet. There is also an increasing amount of evidence that some horses which need extra salt are susceptible to azoturia. Most adult horses will take an extra ounce (25 g) of salt a day in their drinking water quite readily if it is introduced gradually.

Azoturia, or set-fast

Many horse owners are aware that the disease called azoturia is very much connected with feeding. Classically the problem appears when the horse has a day of rest, or reduced work, whilst still having a normal amount of feed. The horse can become very stiff and unwilling to move (hence another name for the condition 'set-fast') because the large muscles of the back and hindquarters are painful. In very acute cases the horse may even go down and be unable to get up on its feet again. On the other hand, there are an increasing number of sub-acute cases, where the affected horse merely sweats more readily than normal when exercised, and so appears less fit than the owner might expect.

What has been thought to happen in azoturia is that the extra food, i.e. the food which is not used to produce energy because the horse is doing less work, is stored in the muscles as a starch called glycogen. When the horse is subsequently exercised, it will use this glycogen as fuel. When it does so, there is a tendency for more lactate to be formed, as a byproduct of energy production, than is usual. We all know that we tend to become wasteful when we have too much of anything. Well, when the horse has an abundance of glycogen available, it tends to obtain its energy in a relatively wasteful way which produces lactate. However, the lactate which is formed cannot be removed quickly enough to prevent it damaging the muscle fibres.

The affected muscles of a horse with azoturia show marked changes. They may be hard and swollen. The damaged fibres leak some of their contents into the bloodstream. In particular two enzymes, called creatine phosphokinase and aspartate aminotransferase, appear in the blood at much higher concentrations than usual. This fact is often used to confirm the diagnosis of azoturia. Similarly a horse cannot be said to have recovered from the condition until these enzyme levels have fallen back to normal (which will not be for some time after the horse appears to have recovered from its clinical symptoms). So, all in all, there is considerable muscle damage caused in azoturia, and for this reason some scientists prefer to refer to the condition as rhabdomyolysis. Whatever the name, the problem is exacerbated by the fact that the swollen muscle fibres and other changes reduce the blood flow through the muscle and therefore reduce the rate at which toxic substances are removed.

At the present time there is a considerable amount of research being carried out into azoturia. We now know, for instance, that it takes days to replace the glycogen used to produce one day's exercise. So a single day's rest should not result in excessive amounts of glycogen being stored away. Even more interesting is the discovery that many horses which appear to be particularly susceptible to the problem are not controlling the levels of minerals such as sodium or phosphorus in the way that they should. They allow too much or too little of such substances to be lost in the urine. The levels of these minerals can have dramatic effects on how the muscles contract because they affect the condition of electrical impulses to the muscle fibres.

This research has led to a major change in how we look at problem cases of azoturia. By comparing the levels of sodium, calcium, etc. in the blood and urine samples taken at approximately the same time, we can see if any problem is present. If it is, we can take appropriate measures to increase the levels fed in the diet. The results can be very dramatic in terms of performance. Even 1 oz (25 g) of salt per day (if that is the treatment indicated for a particular horse) can mean that the horse is able for the first time to do fast work without any muscle damage at all. I must stress that it is not necessarily a fault of the horse's diet which causes such problems, rather an intrinsic fault in the horse's metabolism.

Prevention of azoturia starts by ensuring that a horse's diet always matches its work. So if a horse does less work, it always receives less food. If it does no work, it immediately receives only a maintenance diet of hay and mashes. Owners who can't be bothered to alter their feeding regime until several days after the event deserve what they get. Do avoid also the

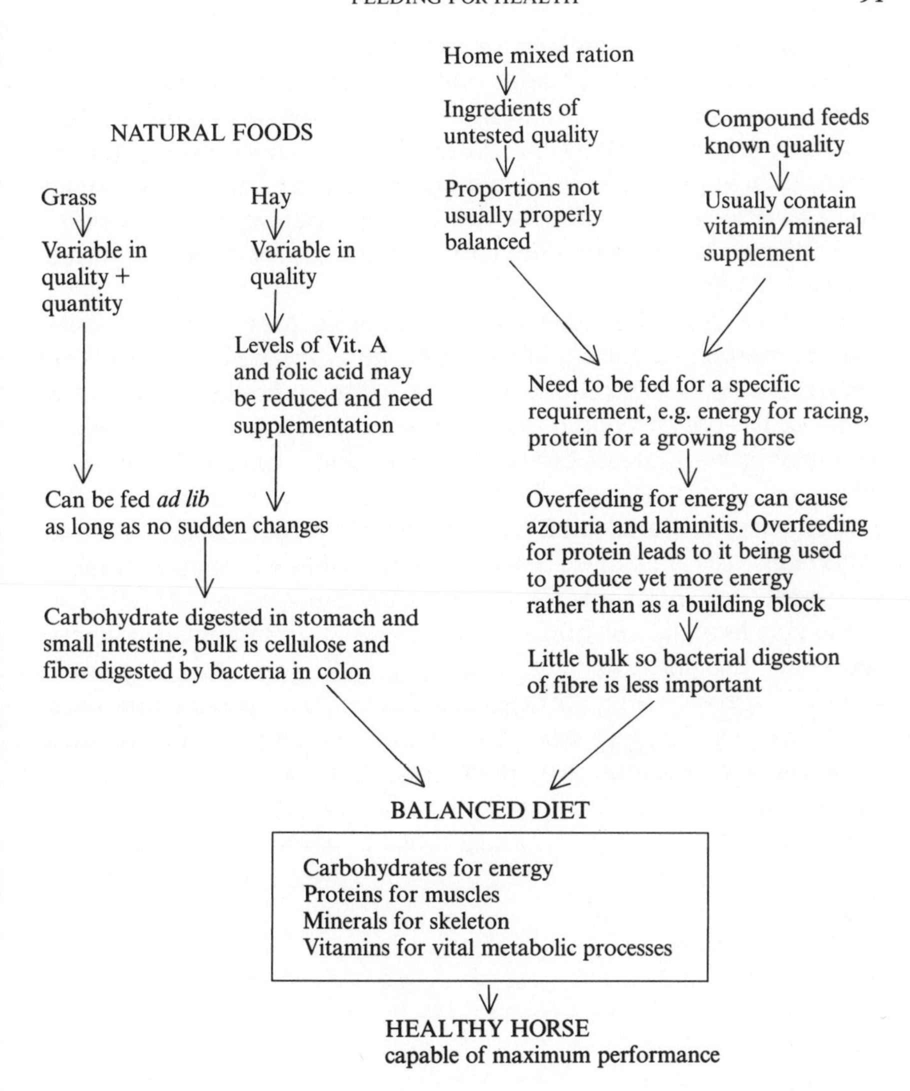

Fig. 5.3 Planning a healthy diet.

temptation to feed more energy than necessary. It is not clever to feed more oats than your neighbour. You should keep reminding yourself that horses have won the Derby on 12 lb (5.5 kg) of oats per day, and is your horse doing anything like that kind of strenuous exercise? Because it is a rapid build-up of toxic substances which occurs in azoturia, a proper warming-up period at the start of exercise can be very beneficial. This opens up the blood supply to the muscles so that removal of toxic substances is as efficient as possible.

It may be helpful to look on azoturia as an abnormal form of muscle fatigue. When a tired horse slows down, one of the main reasons why its muscles are not working is that the levels of lactate in the muscles have become too high. Similarly one of the reasons a fit horse does not tire as easily as an unfit horse is because it has developed a better blood supply to its muscles and so can delay the rate of lactate build-up. Azoturia horses have an altered sensitivity to what constitutes dangerous lactate levels.

Because vitamin E is associated with muscles, people have suggested that giving this vitamin (and its companion, selenium) will speed up recovery from muscle problems such as azoturia. So far no conclusive evidence has been produced to show whether this is or is not the case. It may well be worth doing on the off-chance that it will help a particular horse.

The name azoturia indicates that there are changes in the urine. Affected horses often have dark discoloured urine, which may be due to the presence of substances released from the damaged muscle cells. The horse may have difficulty flushing these substances through its kidneys, and may try unsuccessfully, and apparently painfully, to urinate. Veterinary surgeons may use drugs called diuretics to encourage the horse to urinate. Another approach is to give the horse large volumes of fluids intravenously to flush toxic products away. Veterinary surgeons also use anti-inflammatory drugs to reduce the inflammation in the muscles.

6 Parasites are not necessary

In earlier chapters I have discussed what happens when micro-organisms, i.e. living organisms (such as bacteria and viruses) which are so small that they can only be seen under a microscope, 'invade' a horse. There are, unfortunately, a great number of much larger living organisms which can cause problems. Some of them, such as lice, are visible with the naked eye. Others, such as intestinal worms, may be large enough to see when they are fully grown, but live hidden inside the horse. We often use the word 'parasite' to refer to these creatures, and it might be useful to consider exactly what is meant by that term. A parasite is described as a living organism 'which establishes a physiological association with another living organism, called its host, living either on the surface of, or inside, its host's body, on which it inflicts some kind or degree of injury'.

So parasites always cause some damage. It may not appear to be very serious damage, e.g. loss of hair due to infection with ringworm, but it exists. Most of the damage parasites cause arises from their need to obtain food. This is not always the case, though. As you will see later, intestinal worms can cause serious damage when their bodies 'accidentally' block the hole, or lumen, of blood vessels. It is important to realise that it is not usually in the parasite's interest to actually kill the horse. It may accidentally do so, but once this happens the parasite loses its home because it cannot survive in a dead horse. So the successful parasite weakens its host without killing it. If it can also avoid stimulating the production of any resistance against itself, then so much the better.

Parasitic worms (Helminth)

The first type of parasite I want to discuss is the helminth, or parasitic worm. There are a number of worms which cause problems in the horse, but they all have one important feature in common; they are not contagious and cannot spread from one horse directly across to another. So if you keep a horse which has large numbers of parasitic worms in its intestines in a stable with another horse which does not have any worms, the second horse will not become infected. To infect another horse the worm larvae or eggs that are released in a horse's faeces pass out into the environment. There they undergo certain changes before becoming infective to the horse (either the same horse or a different one). The horse then picks up the infective stage of the worm with the grass it eats. The time it takes before the worm larvae or egg which is passed out on to the pasture can infect another horse varies with each species of worm, and obviously has a considerable bearing on how the worm can be controlled.

Ascarids

Having made those general points, I would like to consider some of the important intestinal worms which affect horses. *Parascaris equorum* is a member of a general family of worms called the ascarids. It is the largest roundworm in horses, and can be nearly 12 ins (30 cm) long. Horses take in ascarid eggs, which hatch in the intestine to release larvae. These larvae them migrate through the horse's body via its bloodstream. They pass through the liver and end up in the lungs. After further changes, or moults, the larvae 'climb up the trachea, or windpipe, to the pharynx at the back of the horse's mouth. They are then swallowed and become adult worms (which can lay more eggs, to be passed out with the droppings, or faeces) in the intestine again. The time which elapses between the horse swallowing the eggs and the new adult worm releasing the first of its eggs is known as the pre-patent period. In the case of *Parascaris equorum*, the pre-patent period is around two to three months.

One feature of ascarid infections in the horse, which does not apply to other worms, is that adult horses develop an immunity to the worm. If you examine faeces samples from adult horses you will hardly ever find ascarid eggs because the horse's immune system knocks out the worms themselves. Foals, however, have not been in contact with the worm long enough to have developed any immunity, and can be infested with large numbers of worms.

Because of their large size, ascarids can all too readily cause blockages of the intestines and of the bile ducts in the liver. Even when they do not stop the passage of food along the intestine though, they can still cause the foal to lose weight because the damaged intestinal wall is not able to absorb feedstuffs properly. Many horse owners are unaware of the fact that ascarids can cause respiratory problems (sometimes referred to as 'summer colds' for obvious reasons). These problems occur when large numbers of migrating larvae reach the lungs at the same time. The foal then starts to cough, it has a high temperature and often a runny nose as well. So it has all the appearances of having a respiratory virus infection. It is important that you appreciate what is really happening, however, because a virus infection will soon pass over, but a heavy ascarid infection will not.

Strongylus vulgaris

Perhaps the most dangerous parasitic worm in the horse is *Strongylus vulgaris*, or the large redworm. This has a very long (6–11 months) life cycle which is so complicated (and unlikely) that it is only in relatively recent years that we have been able to say exactly what happens when a horse becomes infested with this worm. Despite its importance, *Strongylus vulgaris* is nowhere near as large as *Parascaris equorum*; the adult worm is only ¾–2 ins (2–5 cm) long. Like many of the worms I shall be discussing, the life cycle of *Strongylus vulgaris* is adapted so that it spends as little time as possible outside the horse, where it is vulnerable to temperature, drying and being eaten by other animals. So eggs passed out in the droppings have changed to infective larvae in as little as three days. Unlike the ascarids where the infective larvae are swallowed by the horse while still inside the egg, *Strongylus* eggs hatch on the pasture to release their larvae. These climb up the stalks of the grass towards the top, so that even if the horse does not crop the grass very short it will still consume the infective larvae. This clever trick on the parasite's part can be turned to our advantage. If it is possible to 'top' a paddock before you start grazing it, i.e. cut the tops off the grass and other plant stems, then you will reduce the numbers of worm larvae which are sitting there just waiting for your horse to come along and eat them.

Once they have been swallowed, the larvae penetrate the lining of the intestine and move around in the wall until they find an artery. Now arteries, as you will be aware, carry blood from the heart to the tissues, and the blood is pumped along them at considerable pressure. The amazing thing is that once the *Strongylus vulgaris* larvae has managed to penetrate into an artery, it slowly but surely crawls along it against the direction of this fast-flowing blood. The arteries which supply blood to the intestines fan out from a central 'hub', each loop of intestine having its own radiating blood supply. Somehow the worm larvae know when they have reached the hub, because they then stop migrating and settle down for a four-month wait. Eventually the maturing larvae retrace their steps back down the artery and break out into the intestinal tube as adult worms. It takes about six months from the time the *Strongylus vulgaris* larvae are eaten with the grass to the time when they have become adult worms laying more eggs.

How strongyles affect the horse

Strongylus vulgaris is not the only large redworm of horses. *Strongylus edentatus*, *Strongylus equinus* and *Tridontophorus* worms also fall into this category. They have a simpler life cycle, usually only migrating into the intestinal wall for a short time before maturing. The name 'redworm' comes from the fact that the adult worms attach themselves to the lining of the intestines and suck in blood as food, hence their red colour. So if large numbers of worms are present, an appreciable amount of blood will be lost by the horse. This may cause the horse to lose condition and become anaemic.

Surveys in America have associated *Strongylus vulgaris* with up to 80% of the cases of colic diagnosed. Most of these are caused by the migrating larvae partially or completely blocking the arteries supplying the intestines. Deprived of their proper blood supply the intestines do not work as they should. The waves of contraction and relaxation which should move smoothly along their length do not do so, and colic results. Sometimes a length of the intestines may become gangrenous because it is no longer receiving sufficient blood. Many of the acute cases of colic which in the past were blamed on a twisted gut were actually due to these verminous aneurysms, or blood vessels blocked by worm larvae, rather than an actual twist in the intestine.

So worms can cause a recurring mild colic due to either slight damage to the intestinal wall or slight interference with the blood supply. Alternatively they can cause a very acute and fatal colic due to either a section of the intestine becoming gangrenous or to internal haemorrhage when the damaged artery around a larva bursts.

Trichostrongylus axei

The worm with the shortest life cycle is the so-called stomach hairworm, *Trichostrongylus axei*. It takes only three weeks from eggs being passed in the faeces to the larvae becoming egg-laying adult worms back in the horse. The short cycle makes this a particularly dangerous worm for foals because even in their first couple of months of life they can build up large numbers of worms inside their intestines. These worms allow blood to be lost from the inflamed bowel linings, so the foals will develop a bloody diarrhoea which can be very difficult to treat.

Oxyuris equi

The pinworm, *Oxyuris equi*, doesn't really cause any damage to the stomach or intestines. It does have a rather clever 'fail safe' method to make sure it can complete its life cycle, though. The adult female worm lives just inside the horse's anus and comes out on to the skin to lay its eggs. The irritation caused by these female worms causes the horse to rub its tail, and this may knock the eggs off on to the ground where they hatch into larvae which are eaten in the usual way. The horse may, however, lick and bite its tail area, swallowing the larvae without them ever having reached the ground.

All these worms can survive as long as there are horses around and reasonable conditions out on the pasture. So with the possible exception of the pinworm, they will not be a serious problem in horses which are permanently stabled and never go out to graze (once the horse has been 'cleared' of its worms, that is).

Habronema

There are some worms which have what is called an indirect life cycle, where the worm has to pass through another living creature as well as the horse. Such a worm is the large-mouthed stomach worm, *Habronema*. In this case the worm larvae which hatch in the horse's faeces are swallowed by fly maggots. The worm larvae become mature enough to infect a horse at the same time as the maggot becomes an adult fly. The worm larvae are left behind on the horse's lips and nostrils as the flies feed at these places. If the horse licks or swallows them, they can reach its stomach to complete their life cycle. *Habronema* worms can cause problems of the stomach wall if they are present in very large numbers. Even more troublesome is the effect of the larvae if flies leave them in skin wounds. The larvae stop the sores healing, so that they can become infected with bacteria. Even when the wounds do heal in the winter, the *Habronema* larvae have not gone away. They have only migrated into the skin, and the sores will often reappear during the next summer (which is why the condition is called 'summer sores').

Onchocerca

A similar indirect life cycle to that which I have described for *Habronema* worms is followed by the neck threadworm, *Onchocerca*. In this case it is the biting midge, *Culicoides* (also involved in causing sweet itch) which is the intermediate host needed in addition to the horse. The adult *Onchocerca* worms live in rather painful nodules in the horse's ligaments and tendons, especially those of the neck. The larvae, or microfilariae, can cause irritation and dermatitis over most of the body. Normally this worm does not cause very much of a problem in the UK but it was interesting that when large numbers of horses were imported from Eastern Europe several years ago, they were already infested with the *Onchocerca* and very frequently had problems as a result.

Gastrophilus (Bot fly)

For the sake of completeness I ought to mention a parasite which is not really a worm at all, although it lives in the horse's intestinal tract and is often treated as though it is a kind of worm. I am referring to the horse bot, *Gastrophilus*. The bot flies lay their eggs on the hairs of the horse's body, especially the legs. Ths eggs can often be seen as light coloured specks down a horse's legs in late summer time. The horse licks its skin and the larvae which have hatched out burrow their way through the membranes lining its mouth and tongue. After about a month the larvae, as is so often the case with such troublesome internal parasites, migrate through the body to the lining of the stomach. They spend the winter here, looking rather like short, fat maggots. If there are very large numbers of them they can cause ulceration (and even perforation) of the stomach. In the spring the bot larvae let go of the stomach wall, and are swept along and out on to the pasture in the faeces. Unlike worm larvae which then crawl up to the top of the grass stems, the bot larvae burrow into the ground and make a pupa from which the adult fly will emerge in one to three months, i.e. mid-summer again.

With so many different types of worm, and such different types of life cycle, each taking place over a variable time scale, the average horse owner might be excused for despairing of ever managing to control the problems, they cause. While I think it important that horse owners can refer to the peculiarities of particular parasites, because this may have a direct bearing on how we control the parasite, the general principles of worm control are even more important. So I will start with the ideal situation in this respect. As I mentioned earlier, if a worm-free horse is kept in a stable all the time, then it will not acquire any worms. On the other hand, if large numbers of horses are continuously kept on a relatively small area of land over a period of years, then a large worm burden will usually accumulate.

Practical worm control

We have to be practical and design our worm control measures in such a way that they interfere as little as possible with the normal use of our horses. I have to say that the very effective anthelmintics, or drugs which kill worms, which we now have make this task very much easier than it used to be. All horse owners owe a debt of gratitude to the pharmaceutical industry in this regard. Next time you casually worm your horse, spare a thought for what used to happen 50 years ago. At that time the groom might have mixed up a mixture of 1–3 oz (25–75 g) of oil of turpentine, 6 beaten eggs and 1 pint (½ litre) of linseed oil, and given it to the horse as a drench. Other remedies would have been rolled into a ball, and the resultant 'horse ball' given to the horse using a contraption called a balling gun. Sometimes this was nothing more complicated than a hollow tube, one end of which was put into the horse's mouth whilst the groom blew the ball out. The joke was always that you had to blow before the horse coughed, otherwise it was you, rather than the horse, who got the horse ball.

Remedies such as I have described above did not actually kill the worms. They were purgatives which irritated the intestinal walls so much that the horse scoured, or had diarrhoea. With such a rapid movement of contents along the intestine, many of the worms were literally swept away by sheer force of friction. Unfortunately, although this reduced the numbers of worms present, it was often several weeks before the bowel linings recovered sufficiently to work properly again, absorbing nutrients.

So a horse which was purged would lose a good deal of weight, and would often be unable to work for some time.

Thankful as we must therefore be for our modern anthelmintics, we must first of all try to reduce the numbers of worms which our horses take in. Obviously the larger the area of grazing available to each horse, the less likely the horse is to choose to eat a blade of grass carrying a worm egg or larvae. It therefore follows that when large numbers of horses are grazed on a small paddock, worms are likely to be a problem. The advantage of having a large grazing area is an advantage of time and chance rather than of area. There is nothing wrong with several horses grazing a small paddock if they only do so for such a short period of time that the chances of them eating large numbers of worm larvae are small. Ideally they should be moved to another paddock before any eggs which they have passed in their faeces have become infective, i.e. before their infestation perpetuates itself.

This period will vary from worm to worm, depending on the length of its life cycle. As I mentioned, *Trichostrongylus axei* is a particular threat to young horses because its life cycle is only three weeks. *Strongylus vulgaris*, on the other hand, has a life cycle of about six months before the horse will be re-infesting itself. Of course, if the pasture to which you have moved your horse is already heavily contaminated with infective eggs or larvae, then the horse's worm burden will start increasing within a short period. You may not be able to tell that this is happening, because in this early part of the worm's life inside the horse, it will not be releasing any eggs which might be detected in faeces samples. The damage caused by migrating worm larvae is, nevertheless, very real.

With parasites such as *Habronema*, *Gastrophilus* and *Onchocerca*, where flies are an important part of the cycle, then there is no such thing as clean pasture, because flies can appear from some distance away. With the other worms you should be looking for pasture which has not been grazed this season. With the exception of the worms which specialise in attacking young horses, such as ascarids, the larvae and many of the worm eggs are destroyed by a combination of time and climatic extremes such as cold or drying. However, it would be several years before a pasture grazed by horses and then rested could be said to be worm free.

If a paddock becomes very heavily infested with worms it may therefore be quicker to plough the whole paddock up and re-seed it rather than wait for natural wastage to clear it for you. A less drastic measure is to harrow the pasture, which exposes larger numbers of larvae and eggs to the forces of the environment than would otherwise be the case.

Topping the paddock will reduce the number of worm larvae taken in by a horse, because the infective worm larvae tend to crawl up to the top of the grass stems. If the tops of the stems are removed and the horse grazes the remainder then it will pick up fewer larvae. Topping can be carried out mechanically, using a grass cutter of some kind. When it is carried out in this way it is possible for the larvae to climb back up the remaining part of the stem, and any worm eggs which were stuck to the cut grass are still present on the paddock. It is even better if the topping is carried out naturally, using another species of animal to graze the tops off the grass stems. When cattle or sheep eat grass containing horse worm eggs or larvae, the eggs and larvae are killed as they pass through the 'foreign' digestive tract. Incidentally, the same applies in reverse because horses kill any cattle or sheep worms which they might take in. So there is a great deal to recommend the use of cattle or sheep to 'vacuum' clean your horse paddocks. Of course they will not remove all the worms, but they will make a significant difference. There is another advantage as well: horses tend to graze some areas very short but leave others (where they have been dunging) ungrazed. These ungrazed areas become very coarse and contaminated with weeds. Cattle and sheep, on the other hand, graze evenly. They thus compensate for the horse's uneconomic behaviour. When the horses graze the paddock again, they are far more likely to graze the areas which previously they have left, i.e. you have increased the practical grazing area of your paddock.

Choosing a wormer

Although in theory one can keep horses free from worms by control of grazing etc., we very rarely have either a worm-free horse or a worm-free paddock to start from. So invariably we have to use wormers (an illogical name for drugs which kill worms; they should be called anti-wormers). There are a large number of such drugs and it is important that, whichever one you use, you are aware of its strengths and weaknesses. In Table 6.1, I have shown the fields of activity of the wormers at present on sale in the UK. With all these drugs, the dose needed for maximum effect is related to the horse's weight. So you need to know how much, approximately, your horse weighs before you can worm it. A very rough guide is given in Table 6.2, but a relatively precise weight can be obtained from the formula:

$$\text{weight in pounds} = \frac{G^2 \times L}{300}$$

Table 6.1 The activity of the commonly available anthelmintics.

Drug	Ascarids	Adult strongyles	Migrating strongyles	*Oxyuris*	*Trichostrongylus axei*	Bots
Thiabendazole	only at < dose level	Yes	No	Yes	No	No
Pyrantel	Yes	Yes	No	Yes	No	No
Oxibendazole	Yes	Yes	No	Yes	No	No
Mebendazole	Yes	Yes	No	Yes	No	No
Haloxon	Yes	Yes	No	Yes	No	No
Oxfendazole	Yes	Yes	Partial	Yes	No	No
Fenbendazole	Yes	Yes	only at < dose	Yes	only at < dose	No
Metriphonate	Yes	Yes	No	Yes	No	Yes
Fenbantel	Yes	Yes	No	Yes	No	Yes
Dichlorvos	Yes	Yes	No	Yes	No	Yes
Ivermectin	Yes	Yes	Yes	Yes	No	Yes

Table 6.2 What your horse weighs.

Type of horse	Horse's height	Horse's weight
Draught horse	16.0–17.0 hh	1650–2100 lb/750–950 kg
Heavy hunter	15.2–16.3 hh	1300–1550 lb/600–700 kg
Hunter thoroughbred	14.2–16.2 hh	1000–1200 lb/450–550 kg
Arabs	14.0–15.1 hh	900–1100 lb/400–500 kg
Pony	12.0–14.2 hh	650–900 lb/300–400 kg
Small pony	9.0–12.2 hh	450–650 lb/200–300 kg
Donkey	9.0–12.0 hh	500 lb/225 kg

where G is the girth measured in inches just behind the elbow, and L is the length in inches from the point of the withers to the tuber ischii (a body prominence just to the side of the tail). Underdosing is a false economy because you will lose the effect of the drug. Every anthelmintic manufacturer seems to pack their drug for a different weight of horse, so if you are comparing the relative cost of the wormers, do not simply compare a 'pack' of one with a 'pack' of another. You should compare the cost of a dose for your particular horse.

In the UK wormers are usually sold either as a paste (which is packed in a syringe so that it can be squeezed out into the horse's mouth by the owner) or as granules/powder which are mixed with feed. In other countries horse owners appear to have failed to realise that they can safely and efficiently worm horses in this way. They routinely have the anthelmintic administered by their veterinary surgeon using a stomach tube to ensure that it all reaches the stomach. Even when the wormer is to be given by the horse owner, there are pros and cons for paste versus powder. Other things being equal, granules or powders are always cheaper than paste because the plastic syringes used for the paste are relatively expensive. At least with a paste, though, you know straight away whether or not your horse has received a full dose.

The choice of which drug to use is further complicated by the fact that over the years some worms have become resistant to some drugs. When this happens, the offspring of those worms will also basically be resistant to the drug. This drug resistance is especially significant when it involves the strongyles. Quite sensibly, many horse owners seek to avoid this problem by changing the drug they use. In doing so, however, they often make some basic mistakes simply because they don't bother to seek veterinary advice. First and foremost, do you need to change wormers at all? Neither pyrantel nor ivermectin has ever been found to have worms developing resistance. This is despite enormous numbers of doses being used, in the case of pyrantel especially, over many years. Of course, whenever a new wormer is launched, the manufacturers claim that no worms are resistant to it. Unfortunately resistance usually develops to a greater or lesser extent somewhere (especially if large numbers of doses are used).

A careful study of Table 6.1 will reveal that no fewer than five of the drugs (nearly 50% of them in fact) have a name ending in -endazole. This is because they are all variants of the same basic chemical molecule. It would appear that when a worm develops a resistance to one member of this family of drugs, it will often also become resistant to other members of the family. Even if this is not the case initially, it takes relatively little change on the part of the worms to make it so. In other words, the worm's major difficulty is to develop resistance to the basic molecule. If it can do so, it finds it relatively easy to extend that resistance to include other members of the family. So if you are going to change your wormer in an attempt to deal with, or to avoid, a resistance problem, then there is no point at all in changing to another member of the same drug family.

Another way in which people sometimes make mistakes is in the frequency with which they change wormers. Some people use two brands on a regularly alternating basis; some chop and change every time over a range of brands. It is worth looking at what happens when you change wormers if there are any resistant worms present. After worming for the first time you have only resistant worms present. After the second worming you have these same worms plus the resistant proportion of the 'new' worms. Gradually the numbers of resistant worms increase until all the worms are resistant and laying eggs which yield resistant larvae. If you alternate wormers you would expect that when you worm with the second drug you would wipe out all the worms resistant to the first drug. Unfortunately, if you worm every six weeks then you are hoping to achieve a 100% kill of these resistant worms five times during the year, which will not happen. Sooner or later worms resistant to the second wormer appear. This markedly reduces the efficiency of your control programme. With such a large number of alternations every year, you are putting pressure on the worms to develop a resistance to both drugs at once. When that happens there could be a worm explosion. The problem is, what do you do then? Change one or both drugs? As so many of the drugs on sale belong to the same family and so should not be considered as alternatives, it can become difficult to devise an effective worm control programme. There is something to be said for using one wormer for a whole year, or even a bit longer, and then switching to another drug for a similar time. At the end of this period the number of worms which are still resistant to the first drug will be very much reduced, in the same way that a horse which is immune to a disease loses its immunity in time if it has no contact with the disease or its vaccine. It is therefore safe to return to the first drug after this time.

Looking at the overall situation, pyrantel and ivermectin would seem to be the wormers of choice at the moment because no resistance has been shown to them. Because of its activity against migrating strongyle larvae and against bots, ivermectin should certainly be used for the worming carried out around November/December time. It would also be sensible to make use of its anti-larval activity if you are worming a new horse on arrival when you do not know its past history. Pyrantel, on the other hand, can be used to kill tapeworms in horses (which may cause some impactions). So a tapeworm dose (twice the routine dose) might be advisable perhaps once a year, no matter what you do the rest of the time.

Dictyocaulus (Lungworm in horses and donkeys)

There is one worm which I have not so far discussed, namely the lungworm, *Dictyocaulus*. The lungworm which usually causes trouble in horses is the lungworm of donkeys, *Dictyocaulus arnfieldi*, but there is circumstantial evidence that the cattle lungworm can also occasionally cause coughing in the horse.

In the donkey lungworms release eggs. These are removed from the lungs by the cilia, or hairs, which remove mucus. When they reach the pharynx they are swallowed and pass out in the faeces. On the ground they develop until the infective larvae are eaten, when they migrate to the lungs and mature to adult worms. The life cycle takes about four weeks. The lungworm is a very successful parasite of the donkey in that it causes little irritation to the lungs (and so little coughing) and yet can go its own way relatively free from defensive action. It has been suggested that 80% of donkeys are infested with lungworms, but very few show any symptoms. One interesting point is that, quite independently of any other factors, there is a marked increase in the number of lungworm eggs laid in May/early June. So the challenge released on to the paddocks is greatest at that time.

When a horse takes in lungworm larvae, a very different situation develops. The larvae migrate to the lungs, but the vast majority of cases then fail to mature any further when they do so. In most horses the larvae are inhibited in the lungs and never become adults to lay eggs. So although it is relatively easy to find lungworm eggs in donkey faeces it is very unusual to find them in horse faeces. In a few cases the lungworms do mature to adults, and lay eggs in horses. All this does not mean, unfortunately, that lungworms are not much of a problem in the horse. The lungworm larvae are just as much of a 'foreign body' to a horse's lungs as are adult worms. They cause severe irritation to the linings of the small airways where they lie. The horse responds by coughing, producing mucus and possibly constricting the airways around the larvae. Of course these symptoms have great similarities with those produced by COPD. Indeed it has been suggested that up to a third of all COPD cases have some connection with lungworms, although all too often the lungs remain hypersensitive to the irritation of fungal spores and other irritants even after the lungworm problem is removed.

Lungworms should be suspected in any horse which starts to cough whilst it is out to grass. Because it take 12–14 days for the larvae to reach the lungs, the symptoms can arise at any time from 12–14 days after introduction to an infested paddock or close grazing contact with an infected donkey or other animal. Most horse lungworm infections originate from donkeys, although a few come from horses where adult worms have survived and a few come from cattle.

When it comes to treating lungworm, it is as well to start from the premise that 'normal' wormers do not kill the parasite. Fenbendazole is reported to have some activity when used at an increased dose rate. Ivermectin has proved to be effective at the normal rate. With both these drugs the dosage appears to be particularly critical. As owners so often underdose for the actual weight of their horse, when treating specifically for lungworm you must take special care. A drug called levamisole can be useful in treating lungworm. This drug has no effect on any other worms in the horse (although in other animals, especially cattle, it kills a whole range of worms), and so if it is given to a coughing horse and causes a beneficial response then one can be reasonably sure that it really is lungworm which is at the root of the problem. Levamisole is somewhere between fenbendazole and ivermectin in its efficacy. Sometimes these drugs cause a temporary improvement but the horse then relapses. On other occasions, a veterinary surgeon might be sure that lungworm is involved despite an apparent failure of treatment. In such situations it is necessary to pass a tube into the horse's stomach and administer a very large dose of thibendazole (so large that there would be no chance of the horse eating it mixed in food). This remains the treatment most likely to remove all lungworms.

Donkey lovers are understandably rather sensitive about the role of donkeys in the spread of lungworm, especially as their donkeys are usually completely free of symptoms. Nevertheless, the best advice to horse owners must be not to graze their horses with donkeys, or on paddocks which have been grazed by donkeys during the past couple of years. Only if the donkeys have been specifically treated for lungworm every two months for the past year or two can they be considered safe grazing mates for horses. With the present greatly increased usage of ivermectin, this last situation will become increasingly common.

Diagnosing a worm problem

So far I have assumed that your horse has got worms. Before leaving the internal parasites, I want to consider how we find out how many worms of what species are present. Lungworms are a rather special case because it is impossible to say definitely whether a horse does or doesn't carry any. Diagnosis is usually based on whether the horse responds to a treatment which is known to kill lungworms. Strong circumstantial evidence of lungworm infection can sometimes be obtained by examining a sample of diluted mucus taken directly from the horse's trachea, or windpipe. If eosinophil cells are found in the mucus then the horse probably does have lungworm because these cells are not normally present except in association with parasites and/or allergic reactions.

Most worms, however, are diagnosed by finding their eggs in the horse's faeces (and even lungworm can be diagnosed in this way in donkeys). A fresh sample of faeces is examined under a microscope after being treated in such a way as to collect the worm eggs but remove most of the other solid debris. Merely finding worm eggs in a horse's droppings is not necessarily enough to cause concern, though, because almost all horses have worm. A large number of eggs must usually be present before we need to worry because each single adult worm can lay so many eggs, but a single adult worm is not going to have a serious effect on the horse. Your veterinary surgeon's assessment of the significance of a 'worm count' will also have to take into consideration whether the faeces have been diluted by being loose, or concentrated by the horse being slightly constipated. Owners tend to make a mistake over when faeces samples should be collected for worm counts. They should be taken before, not after, worming. Even inefficient drugs can cause worms to temporarily stop laying eggs, thus giving a very misleading negative result. What we really want to know is how successful your control measures have been at reducing pasture contamination in the long term. If you are worming regularly then a faeces sample taken just before worming should still only have low numbers of worm eggs present. When collecting such samples, remember that it is fresh samples which are needed, i.e. faeces which have only just been passed out of the horse and which have not been dried out (or washed out) at all. Your veterinary surgeon only needs a few grams in weight, so he will not thank you if you stagger into the surgery carrying a sackful from each horse.

For *Strongylus vulgaris* a specific blood test has also been evolved. This detects antibodies which the horse might make to *Strongylus vulgaris* larvae and adults, wherever they might be (Fig. 2.4). This test can be quite useful because of the possibility of having large numbers of larvae present but very few adults laying eggs.

One would not expect to see worms in a horse's faeces. After all, they need contact with the bowel wall and blood supply in order to survive. So it is silly to attempt any kind of diagnosis on this basis. Occasionally worms are seen, perhaps reflecting exceptionally large numbers in the bowels or some change in conditions which has forced them to release their hold on the bowel wall. Early wormers, which anaesthetised rather than killed the worms, did result in visible worms in the faeces but the dead worms resulting from modern wormers are usually digested before we get a chance to see them.

External parasites

It is not only intestinal worms which take advantage of a horse's 'generosity'. There are also external parasites which live on (and sometimes under) a horse's skin. As a general rule such external parasites do not pose a threat to a horse's life in the way that internal parasites may do. They may, however, cause considerable discomfort and irritation. A horse rubbing itself because of a skin irritation is more obviously ill to a casual observer than one with a large worm burden.

Sweet itch

Biting midges are not specialised parasites of the horse. They land on the horse only to take a quick mouthful of blood and then fly off again. Their life cycle is therefore of no real interest. Indeed it might be said that they cause absolutely no harm to the horse. I have included them here because they sometimes stimulate a horse to cause harm to itself. Some horses become hypersensitive to the bites (especially the saliva) of these insects. When this happens the affected area of skin becomes intensely irritating, and the horse rubs itself vigorously in an attempt to relieve the irritation. Such a horse is said to have sweet itch. The midges, especially those of the *Culicoides* family, concentrate their bites on the upper parts of the horse. An affected horse usually rubs its mane and tail areas and may continue to do so until all the hairs have been broken off and the skin is swollen, raw and weeping. It really is amazing how much self-inflicted damage such horses can cause themselves. Because it is a hypersensitive response to insect bites, sweet itch disappears during the cold winter months when the midges are killed off. May and September are the worst months because the temperature and humidity are then at their most favourable to the midges. Unfortunately hypersensitivity is usually a permanent state, so that once a horse has developed sweet itch, it will continue to do so every succeeding year.

There is no way in which you can prevent your normal horse from becoming hypersensitive and developing sweet itch. You can only draw some comfort from the fact that the vast majority of horses stay trouble-free in this respect. There is also no way of detecting whether an apparently normal horse which you are buying 'out of season' has sweet itch or not. It might pay, however, to be very suspicious of any horse which has a hogged mane (the equine equivalent of a crew cut). The mane may have been cut to hide the fact that the hairs were short and uneven following a summer attack of sweet itch.

Lice infestations

Many horse owners find the thought of their horses being infested with lice repugnant. If told that such an infestation is the cause of their horse developing bald patches where it has rubbed itself, they will not rest until treatment has been carried out. Yet, in fact, there must be millions of lice on our horses without us ever knowing that they are there. Lice are parasites of the skin, where they feed by biting or by sucking blood. They lay their eggs attached to the hairs and their life cycle lasts three to five weeks. They can only survive for up to a week off the horse, and so they must be present all the year round. Despite this, symptoms (and owner worry) only usually develop in cold weather.

Lice cause marked irritation; the horse will often rub itself until it is bald or even red raw. The neck, shoulders and hindquarters seem to be the areas most likely to be involved. Sometimes lice are held to be responsible for a horse losing condition; on the other hand, lice are generally more likely to cause irritation in horses in poor condition anyway. Lice can be killed by using drugs such as gamma benzene hexachloride in powder or wash form, but treatment will need to be repeated every week or so because it is so difficult to kill the eggs which have already been laid. Although lice can only survive for a short period away from the horse, that still allows them to be spread by physical transfer on tack and grooming equipment. Before searching for a culprit which might have infested your horse though, do remember that most likely you are not dealing with a new problem, but with an infestation which has been present for some time without showing symptoms.

Mange mites

Another skin parasite is the mange mite. There are three families of these which can trouble the horse: sarcoptic, psoroptic and chorioptic mites.

The first two are notifiable diseases in Great Britain, i.e. if they are suspected the fact has to be notified to the Ministry of Agriculture because it is thought they no longer occur here. Like lice they are permanent parasites of the horse which cause most trouble in the cold winter weather. Their life cycle spans one to two months. Mange mites burrow into the top layers of skin. There they naturally cause marked irritation. So symptoms can range from just rubbing to oozing patches of bare skin. The different species tend to affect different parts of the body; chorioptic mange, for example, most commonly affects the skin on the back of the fetlock.

Treatment must again be repeated weekly to kill off larvae hatching out. There are a number of effective drugs available, e.g. bromocyclene. Because chorioptes can live for up to ten weeks away from the horse, treatment must be continued long after any symptoms have disappeared. If a horse does become infested, the stable must also be treated. At least three weeks' rest must be allowed afterwards for it to become trouble-free.

It will be obvious that the stable/horse box environment, the riding tack and the grooming equipment can all be involved in spreading skin parasites. Horse owners often keep their tack clean, sometimes keep their grooming kit clean, but rarely disinfect their horse box or stable. The horse box in particular is often forgotten as a source of trouble, which is silly because owners quite frequently allow their horses to travel in other people's transport without having any idea as to whether 'infected' horses have been carried in it previously.

Ringworm and its spread

One disease which is often spread in this way is ringworm. Horses can pick up the infection during a short journey, even though the symptoms might not appear for weeks afterwards. Strickly speaking, ringworm is a skin fungus, rather than what we normally refer to as a skin parasite. It would seem appropriate, however, to discuss it here because the hygiene methods which should be applied are common to all these skin problems.

The fungus grows in the skin itself but comes to affect the coat hairs. Weakened, these break off (rather than being rubbed off as happens in a louse infestation, for example) leaving bare, crusted areas. The name ringworm comes from the fact that the bare areas are often circular in shape, but the areas can be other shapes, and one cannot make a precise diagnosis simply on whether or not a bare area of skin is round or not. Laboratory confirmation of the disease may take several days, so it is often necessary to take a pessimistic view and treat the horse as if it is ringworm before a precise diagnosis has been reached. Delay in starting treatment will permit the disease to progress further and may allow it to spread to other horses.

With time most horses recover from ringworm. As this takes three to six months, and as most ringworm spreads during the winter stabling period, it may appear that the act of turning the horse out to grass has led to a cure. Do not be misled by such old wives' tales: it is not the grass which causes a cure, anymore than sunlight 'cures lice', it is just the natural pattern of the disease. There are three main types of treatment for ringworm. The fungus can be killed off by special antibiotics, especially griseofulvin. These accumulate in the skin, where they can kill the fungus. A completely different approach is to wash the horse (and preferably its tack and stable) with a fungicide. The latter method is not as effective at killing the fungus as the oral treatment, but may be more effective at stopping its spread. So the ideal treatment is a combination of the two methods.

It is difficult to avoid the introduction of ringworm into a yard because

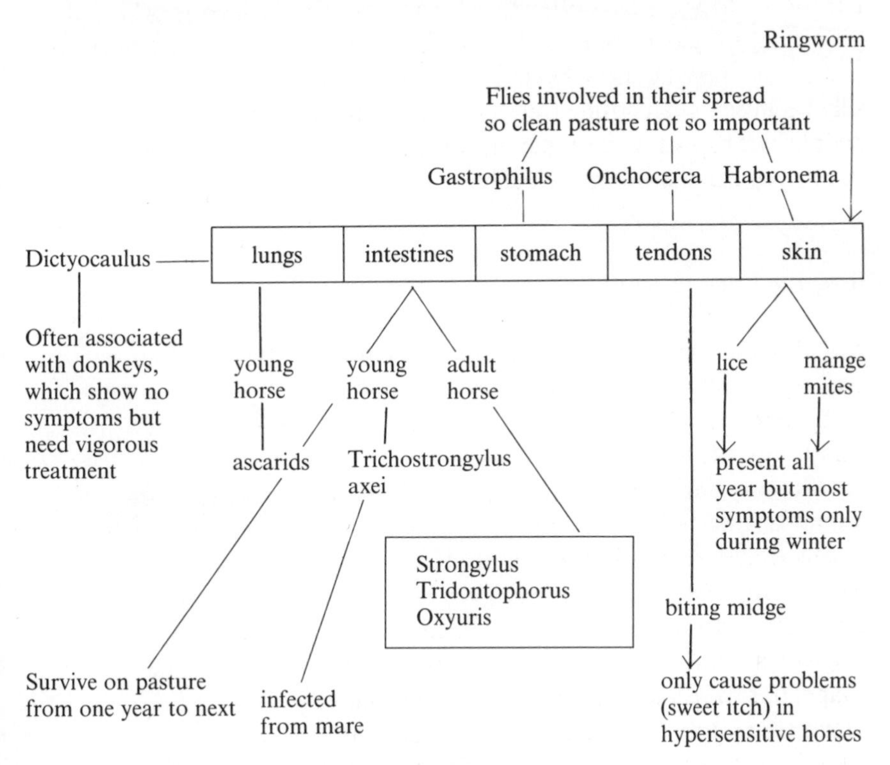

Fig. 6.1 Parasites of the horse.

it can be so easily picked up by casual contact with horses, tack or stabling. It is possible, however, to take active measures to stop its spread within a group of horses. All horses should be washed with a suitable fungicide, even if they do not appear to have the disease. Of course, this may be 'shutting the door after the horse has bolted' because these horses may be already incubating the fungus. Affected horses must be kept away from any contact, however indirect, with other horses. Ringworm cannot spread via the air, like an influenza virus, but must be carried. No tack, grooming kit, feeding utensils, etc. from affected horses must be allowed to come into contact with unaffected horses. The ringworm spores can survive on such items for 12 months unless they are killed off by a suitable disinfectant.

So there are a whole range of parasites which can affect our horses. They vary in size and effect, but all have at least one thing in common: their presence is undesirable. Unfortunately there are no vaccines available as yet to protect horses against parasitic diseases, so it is not possible for the horse owner to hand over responsibility for avoiding trouble to a pharmaceutical company. Instead constant vigilance and preventive measures must be taken, and veterinary advice will be needed to tailor such a preventive medicine scheme to your particular situation.

7 Fit to compete

It is interesting that we tend to interchange the words 'fit' and 'healthy'. If we ask how somebody is, they might well answer 'Oh, pretty fit', when they mean that they are healthy. I am not at all sure that the two words are interchangeable. It is possible for a racehorse to be completely healthy as it grazes in a field, but you could not say that it was fit to race. Fitness might be defined as having a horse sufficiently prepared, or ready, for a particular athletic activity so that the horse has 'a chance of competing successfully against other animals of equal standing', as Dr David Snow, head of the Animal Health Trust's Exercise Physiology Unit at Newmarket, puts it. (The process of getting a horse fit is known as 'conditioning' in the USA.)

Fitness is not an absolute term with a single value. You cannot say a horse is fit and mean that it is fully prepared for any activity, because the demands of the various disciplines are so very different. A horse will need different preparation for a long-distance ride than it will for a 5-furlong (1000 m) sprint. Nor will the fittest horse always win. A horse with more basic ability may still beat a less talented but fitter opponent. The nearer you get to the top of the tree in any particular type of competition, the more likely it is that all the competitors will be near the peak of their fitness. Small differences in fitness may then make the distinction between success and failure.

The balance between fitness and over-training

Small differences in preparation can also tilt the balance from peak fitness to being 'over-trained'. This is a peculiar state where performance declines the harder you try to improve it. The horse blows hard after exercise and sweats profusely, just as you might have expected it to do if it had not had any training at all. It is rather like a piece of elastic which suddenly loses all its elasticity when it is overstretched. We get a clue as to what is happening inside the horse if we look at some of the indications of muscle fatigue and function. The by-products which cause fatigue, or tiredness, by building up in the muscles seem to be permenently present, rather than washed away by the bloodstream within an hour or so. It is as if the horse is fatigued before it has done any exercise at all. Nowadays there is a tendency to blame 'the virus' for a horse's lack of success rather than admit that one has over-trained the horse. It is hoped that both problems will right themselves with rest.

The reason why I am dealing with equine fitness in a book entitled *How to Keep Your Horse Healthy* is that people keep their horses to ride. Sooner or later most riders put athletic stress of some kind on their horse, and a fit horse is less likely to become subject to fatigue-related injuries than an unfit one. So many lamenesses have their origin in a careless, uncoordinated movement which puts too much stress on an already tired part of the horse's anatomy.

Fitness is a relatively transient thing. A couple of days can completely alter a horse's level of fitness. Having said that, fitness alters more quickly for the better than for worse. Many owners expect that if a fit horse has to stay in its stable for a couple of days, its fitness will deteriorate immediately and rapidly. This is not the case. Most horses will be able to maintain a reasonable level of fitness for 7–14 days of rest as long as the feeding programme is handled sensibly. Only at the most sophisticated levels of fitness will a noticeable deterioration occur during short periods of rest.

Training programmes

The horse owner aims to achieve a suitable level of fitness for the type of activity he intends to undertake. In order to do this, a training programme has to be decided upon. When doing so, there are four aspects which must always be considered: energy requirements, structure, skill and acclimatisation. The relative importance of these factors will vary. For example, racing and long-distance rides will obviously need far more energy than dressage. Conversely, dressage and show jumping need more attention to skill training than racing. Unfortunately it is not possible to lay down strict training programmes which will bring out the best in every single horse. The programme always needs to be adapted to each individual. So if you follow a particular programme successfully with one horse, it does not follow that it will work with its next-door neighbour. For decades the horse world has been infatuated with the Newmarket style of training, i.e. building up steady slow cantering every day with faster work only twice a week. Only (literally) in the last year or so have people had the courage to question scientifically whether this is the best form of training for their particular needs. The answer may well be no.

Training to improve energy production is aimed at putting off that moment when the horse starts to feel tired. The pain and weakness that we call fatigue or tiredness, are caused by the horse's muscles needing more energy than they can obtain from the fuel they have available. Energy production can be improved in two ways. Firstly the fuel supplies can be increased. Obviously feeding affects fuel supplies. Increasing the carbohydrate part of the ration increases the fuel from which energy can be obtained. But that is only like stockpiling coal at the coal mine while the power station uses its last reserves. Transport is the key to the problem. The horse's muscles obtain their fuel via their blood supply, and training increases that blood supply. That is not to say that there are specific routines which can cause the horse to increase the number or size of the arteries supplying its muscles. Regular muscular work at a particular level of intensity will eventually lead to the development of the necessary blood supply. But if the demands are made before the supply exists, the system grinds to a halt before the winning post.

The body never builds an arteriole network which supplies more blood than there are veins to remove it. So if training increases the blood supply, it also increases the waste-product removal system. This is important in relation to fatigue, because much of the pain associated with fatigue is thought to be caused by the high levels of lactic acid which accumulate. Improved removal in a fit horse lowers this lactic acid, so enabling the muscles to carry out more work before fatigue arises.

The second way in which training improves energy is by increasing aerobic capacity. This is a rather important concept which is central to the whole idea of training. Each muscle fibre has a system of chemicals called enzymes which break down fat and sugars (i.e. fuel) to release energy. The muscle then uses this energy to replace the energy involved in contracting. The whole system works most efficiently in the presence of oxygen, because then the amount of toxic waste products produced is very small. This energy production in the presence of oxygen (which is supplied by the bloodstream) is called aerobic metabolism. It is possible for the muscle system to work without oxygen, but when it does so a large amount of lactic acid is produced. If this lactic acid is not immediately removed by the bloodstream, then, like any other acid, it will cause damage to the muscles. Energy production which produces lactic acid because of a lack of oxygen is called anaerobic metabolism. It is obviously beneficial that when we ask a horse to perform any work, as much as possible of the energy expended should be obtained aerobically. If the horse can do so, then it will not show any signs of fatigue. The whole aim of training is to avoid the potentially undesirable effects of fatigue, i.e. to increase the capacity of the horse to obtain its energy aerobically.

Another way in which we hope training helps to avoid injuries is by altering the structure of bones and tendons. Owners talk in terms of a fit horse having good hard tendons, rather than soft tendons, for instance. Scientifically there is little evidence to back this up, but that is probably due to our inability to measure such changes, rather than any lack of effect. Bone certainly changes when not subjected to the regular stress of exercise. This can be seen in human hospital patients who have had prolonged bed rest, and is also a problem in astronauts. The changes are associated with the density of bone, i.e. with the concentration of minerals such as calcium and phosphorus present.

We all know that practice makes perfect. The more often we perform a particular action, the less likely we are to make mistakes, and the more quickly we are able to carry it out. This is because the nerve pathways carrying messages to the muscles involved become almost programmed to follow a particular sequence. We can improve a horse's skill by training, but only up to its natural ability level. No amount of training will make a horse successful if it does not have the natural ability. We also have to remember another proverb, namely that familiarity breeds contempt. This is especially noticeable with jumping. If a horse repeatedly jumps exactly the same course of jumps, there comes a time when accuracy starts to decrease rather than increase.

So familiarity is not always advantageous when related to a relatively precise action. There can be no doubt, however, that it does result in the horse being more relaxed when it is being asked to perform in familiar circumstances. A relaxed horse does not waste unnecessary energy, and so has more energy left for the competition etc. On the racecourse it is generally considered unwise to bet on a horse which is so excited that it starts to sweat profusely even before the start of the race. Such horses all too often fail to live up to expectations during the race.

Measuring fitness

Once you are convinced that a fit horse is less likely to suffer injuries, it becomes important to have some means of measuring fitness. In the absence of such means, one runs the danger of finding out the hard way that a horse is not fit enough for the work it has been asked to do. One might think that the obvious way to assess fitness is to time how quickly the horse can perform a set amount of work. This method is used in some racehorses, comparing the times taken to complete a measured gallop. It is rarely used in the UK, due perhaps to a failure of the conservative racing industry to appreciate how sophisticated timing systems can now be.

When a horse pulls up after exercise, everybody accepts that a horse which is breathing very quickly must be less fit than one which is breathing more slowly. This is because an unfit horse has to use more anaerobic metabolism than a fit one. The result is that more lactic acid is produced in the unfit horse, and after the exercise stops, a large amount of oxygen must be 'consumed' in the course of neutralising that acid. One advantage of using respiration as a guide to fitness is that it does not need much in the way of equipment. The respiratory rate can be counted either whilst still riding or after dismounting. In an unfit horse the respiratory rate per minute may either be much faster than in a fit horse which has performed the same work, or it may take very much longer to slow down after the exercise. When a horse is standing quietly in the stable, it only takes one breath for every three heart beats. Anaerobic metabolism can break this link, however, until the horse might even end up taking two breaths for every one heart beat. In some long-distance riding events the respiratory rate after the ride compared with the heart rate determines whether the horse is eliminated or not.

Although the respiratory rate may be easier to measure, the horse's heart rate is probably a more reliable measure of its fitness. The heart rate is not measured by counting the pulse rate, because this can be rather tricky to do. It can be counted using a stethoscope to amplify the heart sounds. This is relatively easy but it can only be used after the exercise. The heart rate adjusts to new circumstances very rapidly, so that even a few seconds trotting or delay before counting will result in a false reading. In recent years electronic heart beat monitors have become available (Fig. 7.1). These measure the heart rate not by sound but by using the electrical changes which occur in the body as a result of electrical changes inside the heart as it beats. These meters provide a continuous read-out of the heart rate, either for the rider or for analysis by the trainer at a later time.

Fig. 7.1 An electronic heart beat monitor.

We often take a horse's healthy resting heart rate to be around 20–40 per minute. A fit horse has a lower heart rate than an unfit horse even before it puts a foot out of the stable. Excitement, not surprisingly, causes a rapid increase in heart rate. Exercise causes the heart rate to increase directly proportionally to the severity of the exercise. At the gallop, for instance, the heart rate may exceed 250 beats per minute. When we use heart rates to measure fitness, we can do it in two ways. Either we can see the amount of work the horse can do before its heart rate exceeds a chosen figure, or we compare the heart rate which results from an identical amount of work on different occasions. If one is careful to compare like with like it has even been possible to detect the very early stages of pain, such as lameness, by seeing an increase in the daily heart rate.

There is sometimes a tendency to confuse fitness with fatness. A fit horse is never a fat horse, but it might well be a thin horse. In fact each horse has a weight at which that horse is able to give its best performance. It can be difficult to find this weight, because it can only be done by trial and error, but once you have done so the knowledge is very useful. The weight varies surprisingly little, even over the years. The majority of horses entered for competitions are probably overweight, just as the majority of people in the developed world are overweight. Although a horse is most accurately weighed on a weighbridge, a very reliable estimate can be obtained from easy-to-take measurements. As described earlier, the formula is as follows:

$$\text{weight in pounds} = \frac{G^2 \times L}{300}$$

when G is the girth measured in inches just behind the elbow, and L is the length in inches from the point of the withers to the tuber ischii (a bony prominence just to the side of the tail).

The link between blood tests and fitness

Much has been written about and much money spent on examining a horse's blood in an attempt to assess fitness and health. All three parts of the blood are considered: the red cells, the white cells and the fluid plasma. As anaemia is rare in the horse, the red cell numbers are not as important as might at first seem likely given their vital role in the body. The packed cell volume (PCV) or the proportion of red blood cells to fluid in the blood, may be significant. It will indicate whether dehydration is present. All measurements involving red blood cells are significantly changed by even slight degrees of excitement. This is because the horse's spleen contains literally millions of red blood cells which are instantly pumped into the system if adrenaline levels rise.

White cells can provide clues as to the presence of infections which may depress performance. For the results to be of any value, however, the samples must always be obtained at the same time of day. First thing in the morning, before feeding and exercise, or in the late afternoon are said to be the most ideal times for blood testing. The more past values you

Table 7.1 How the packed cell volume changes.

Activity	PCV	Heart rate
Resting	36	36
Eating	40	
Travelling in horsebox	40	
Walking	42	60
Excited	48	80

have available with which to compare a sample, the more significant any differences will be. So there is a limit to the amount of information which can be obtained from a single sample taken after you suspect something has gone wrong, because you have nothing worthwhile to which you can compare it. White cells levels are low on the day after exercise, which may make it look as if the horse has a virus infection.

Plasma enzyme levels can provide a great deal of information about illnesses affecting the internal organs. They can also help in assessing fitness, because the levels of muscle-active enzymes stay very steady in a fit horse. The interpretation of the levels of enzymes such as creatine phosphokinase, aspartate amino transferase and gamma glutamyl transferase is obviously outside the scope of this book. By and large, enzyme levels increase with training before falling back when fitness is achieved. In other words, training consists of repeated stress and slight damage to which the horse's body responds until the adaptations can cope with the tasks set. The distinction between a raised level due to training and a raised level due to disease or injury can sometimes be a very blurred one.

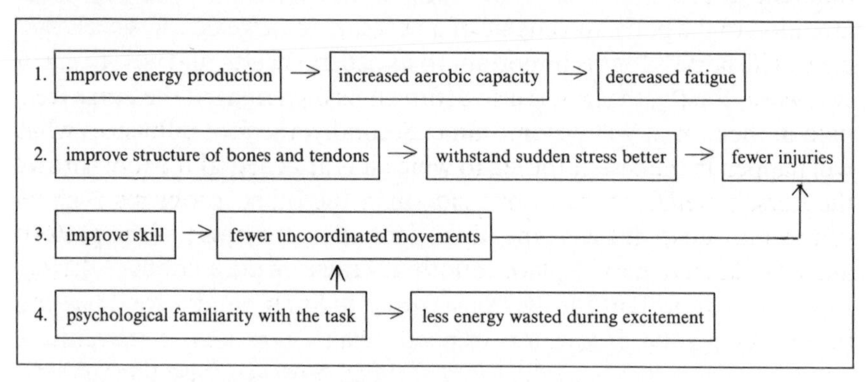

Fig. 7.2 Summary of aims of training.

8 Looking after your horse's feet

There is a well-known saying, 'no foot – no horse'. It is an obvious statement but one that can so easily be forgotten. Modern man is no different in this respect than his ancestors. After all, we still pay more attention to the body and engine of a new care than we do the wheels and tyres. The horse's foot is important to its general health and well-being in two ways. Firstly, the foot is a structure in its own right. If the horse feels pain in the foot, it will become lame. Secondly, the foot influences what will happen in the rest of the leg to which it is attached. If the foot throws the horse's weight more to one side than the other, problems such as splints may arise. If the shape of the foot alters the angle of the pastern and fetlock, then this will place abnormal strains on the tendons of the leg. I think it is important for the horse owner to know what a good healthy foot looks like. Of course, lots of people claim to be able to recognise a good foot when they see one. Most of them, however, base their criteria solely on whether the horny hoof is smooth and without any cracks or horizontal ridges. The shape of the hoof is much more important than such cosmetic features.

The structure of the healthy foot

Have you ever tried to describe the shape of a horse's hoof to a blind person? It is incredibly difficult to put it into words. Given this peculiar shape, there are several measurements that can be made to check that the foot is properly 'balanced'. By balanced I mean that the shape of the foot ensures that the weight of the horse is borne in the centre of the sole, not

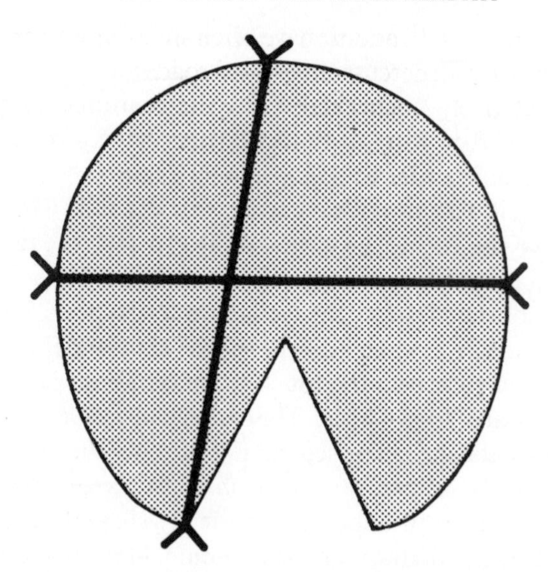

Fig. 8.1 The balanced foot. A line drawn from the middle of the toe to the corner of the heel is exactly the same length as a line drawn across the widest part of the foot.

to one side or the other, neither too far forward or back. Figure 8.1 shows that a line drawn from the heel/wall junction to the centre of the toe should be almost exactly the same length as one drawn across the widest part of the foot. If this line is longer than the width, then the foot is too long at the toe. If it is shorter than the width then it may be that the toe has been cut too short; it may, on the other hand, be that the side walls of the foot have been allowed to spread outwards more than normal.

In Fig. 8.2 you can see the effects these abnormalities may have on the horse's leg as a whole. In a properly balanced foot the weight of the horse (which is assumed to pass down the centre of the pastern bones) will be in the centre of the foot. If the toe is too long, then this weight is moved backward towards the heel area, which is not adapted to withstand it. Even a non-horsemen can see that when we look at such a foot, the front wall diverges from an imaginary line drawn down the centre of the pastern. In the balanced foot, the front wall of the hoof is parallel to such an imaginary line. If the toe is too short, then the horse's weight is moved forwards. The front wall then appears to converge with our imaginary line.

Wild horses manage remarkably well to maintain a balanced foot. Wear and tear, including the breaking off of the weight-bearing edges of the hoof, counteract the continuous growth of horn which takes place from the coronet downwards. Our domesticated horses do not fare so well. Their relative lack of exercise means that often the horn is growing faster then it is worn away. In addition we often shoe our horses to protect them from the friction and percussion of hard roads and so on. As a result the hoof grows relatively unchecked. Over the centuries (and the first farriers date from before Roman times) farriers have grown skilled at trimming horse's feet in order to balance them again.

There are two pitfalls into which some farriers fall. The first is a tendency to allow the toe to grow too long. In fact the same effect sometimes arises because they trim the heels too short. The result of this is, as I have mentioned, to throw the weight on to the heels. Apart from the internal structures, everyone knows that the heel is the most flexible part of the foot. If asked to bear too much strain for a considerable length of time, the heel starts to collapse. This fault can be very difficult to remedy once it is established. The second pitfall arises during shoeing. If a horse has a perfectly shaped foot, it is obviously wrong to alter that shape in order to make it fit a less than perfectly shaped or sized shoe. From this has developed the admirably sound idea that one should always alter the shoe to fit the foot. This idea fails down when dealing with an already less than perfect foot. By making the shoe fit the foot, one is losing the opportunity to correct the fault and may encourage it to

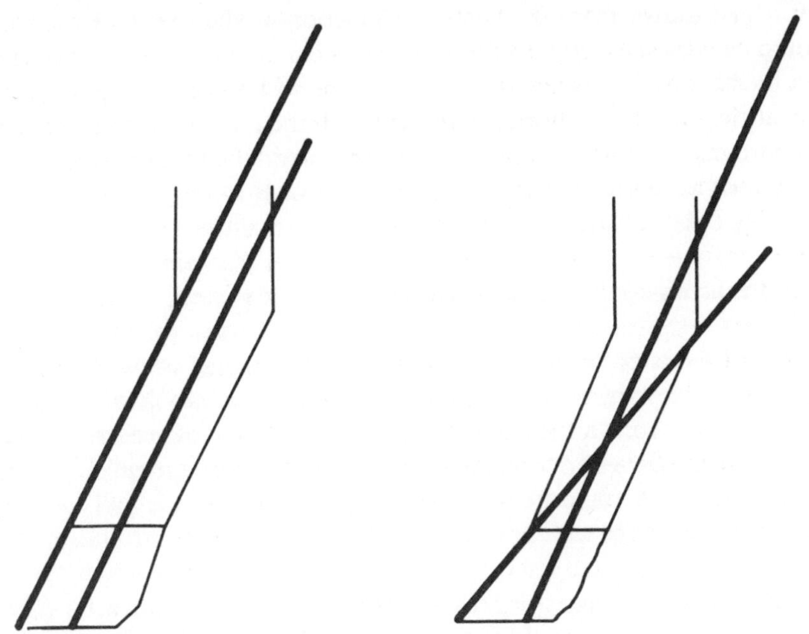

Fig. 8.2 The hoof-pastern axis. Notice how a line drawn up the front edge of the hoof should be parallel to a line drawn down the centre of the pastern. When the toe is too long, the two lines converge, and the weight of the leg is thrown towards the heel rather than the centre of the hoof.

deteriorate further. If the foot is not shaped properly it is better to fit the shoe so that it is slightly more ideally shaped. Despite what some people might expect, the horse's foot will then grow to fit the shoe. So if one fits a shoe which is, say, $\frac{1}{6}$ in. (4 mm) too wide, the horse's foot will spread to cover it. If, however, one fits a shoe $\frac{1}{6}$ in. (4 mm) too narrow, then the foot will tend to shrink back to the size of the shoe.

It is worth remembering that even with the best farrier in the world, a horse will only be properly shod for a maximum of 16 weeks of the year. This is because horses are not usually shod more often than every six weeks. Within two weeks of being shod, however, the growth of the hoof will have undone some of the 'good' achieved by the farrier and the horse will be acceptably, rather than perfectly, shod. I mention this because it emphasises the importance of ensuring that a horse is not left too long between shoeings. It is not a case of the foot only starting to grow out of the shoe after six or eight weeks, whichever frequency of shoeing one uses. It is growing away from the shoe from the day after the shoe is nailed on. Another factor worth considering is that if, unfortunately, the foot is improperly prepared, it might be a lot less than six weeks before the horse ought to be shod again. Thankfully the standard of farriery in the UK is improving all the time as a result of the splendid work of organisations such as the Worshipful Company of Farriers. Perhaps horse owners who live in areas which are still poorly served in this sphere will be interested to know that the Farriers Registration Council are attempting to encourage farriers to move into such areas. Some horse owners have had to put up with a take-it-or-leave-it attitude from their farrier for too long.

The effects of poor quality horn around the hoof wall

Certain horses seem particularly prone to developing cracks along the bottom of the hoof wall. Quite large pieces of horn can break off from here without any warning. In many cases, especially in unshod horses, this is due to the hoof growing too long. A closer examination will reveal that what appeared to be solid hoof was actually only about $\frac{1}{2}$–$\frac{3}{4}$ in. (12–18 mm) thick because the hoof wall had grown down past the sole. Poor shoeing, especially in respect of the fitting of the shoe and the nails, can also predispose to such breaking away of horn. There are, however, some horses where there is a physiological reason for the problem.

Horn consists of tubules of a protein, called keratin, linked together. It would appear that two chemicals, namely D.L. methionine and biotin are vitally important in maintaining the strength of these chemical bonds between the horn tubules. Although it might not be correct to say that it is simply a deficiency of these two substances which causes weak horn, practical experience has shown that when the problem does exist it may be helped by feeding a D.L. methionine and/or biotin supplement. Such treatment will not, of course, have any effect on the existing horn because the bridges in this have already been manufactured. So it will be several months before any improvement is seen in the hoof wall. As horn grows at the rate of about 1 in. (25 mm) every four to six weeks, you can work out how long it will take for the new, improved horn to grow down the wall from the coronet, where it is formed, to the ground where it is worn away.

Sometimes a really deep crack forms in the hoof wall. Because of the strong twisting forces which develop in the hoof when the horse moves, these cracks can get longer and longer. Indeed, they may extend all the way from the ground to the coronet. Certainly when such a sandcrack, as it is called, does extend up to the coronet, it will not heal without help because the horn tubules will be being torn apart as soon as they are formed. For this reason you should never ignore sandcracks, even if they are quite short ones. Once they grow more than 1 in. (25 mm) long they become self-perpetuating flaws. In addition to being a blemish, they may make the horse lame. This is because they can extend right through the thickness of the hoof wall so that the two sides of the crack pinch the underlying, sensitive tissues of the foot.

There are a variety of ways of treating a sandcrack. One is to make a horizontal groove in the hoof at the top of the crack, so that the crack can spread no further (Fig. 8.3a). This will only work if the groove is made at least as deep as the crack itself. All too often the groove is a superficial affair, and the sandcrack spreads underneath it – these cracks are deeper than many people think. Another approach is to make parallel grooves on either side of the sandcrack in order to lessen the tension on the crack (Fig. 8.3b). If these methods fail, or if the crack is a particularly bad one, then a more drastic approach is needed. This involves cutting out the sandcrack and any decaying horn around it, and keying into the resulting groove an acrylic horn replacement material. When this sets hard it completely immobilises the crack and prevents it spreading. The acrylic material will be gradually removed during routine foot trimming as the hoof grows.

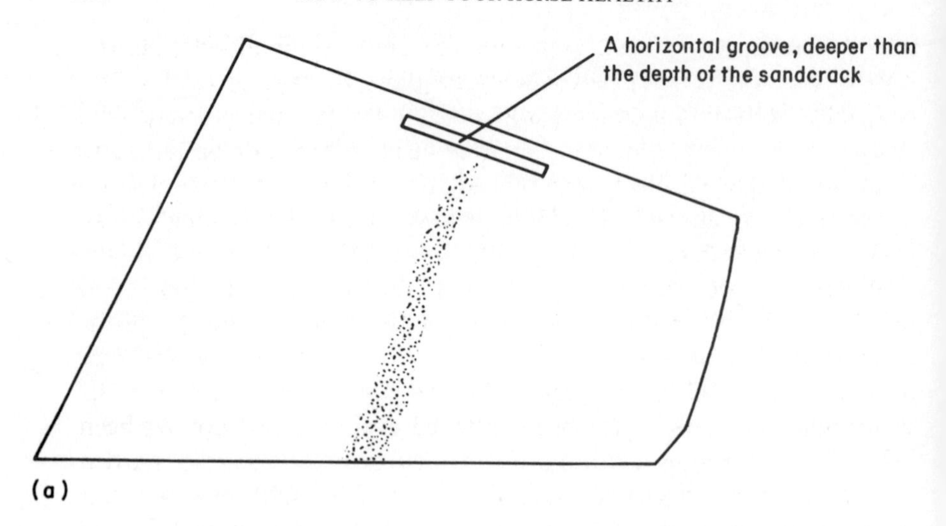

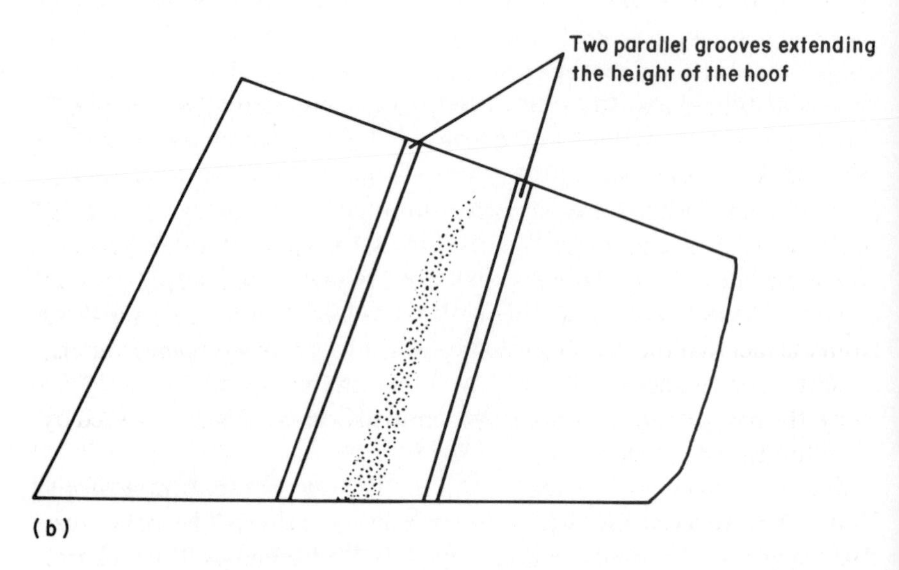

Fig. 8.3 Treating a sandcrack.

Neglect of the horny hoof

The horn of a horse's hoof appears to be very hard and strong. Amazing as it might seem, its main weakness is water. Prolonged contact with moisture softens the horn. The soft moist horn can then very readily become infected with bacteria. This can happen in a sandcrack when the surface waterproofing layer has been broken and mud becomes packed into the crack. If a horse is kept standing in damp conditions, the soft horn of the frog and the grooves alongside it can become infected. This is especially likely to happen if a horse is stabled on damp urine-soaked straw because the ammonia in the urine helps to break down the horn. The result is very soft black horn which has a foul smell. Such an infection is referred to as 'thrush'. If the infection penetrates deep enough it can make the horse lame.

Whenever horn becomes infected, the first step you must take is to remove all the affected horn. Not one speck of black horn should be allowed to remain because if you leave even a small area behind, the infection may well spread again. In the case of thrush, where the surrounding horn will have been softened even if it has not yet been infected, then a dilute solution of formaldehyde may be used to harden and dry the horn (as well as to kill off any infection remaining). Needless to say, there is no point in doing all this unless you ensure that the stable hygiene is put right as well.

I have already stressed the importance of ensuring that your horse is well shod. Shoes are fitted so that they support the wall of the hoof and do not press on the sole. If a shoe is poorly fitted and is too narrow, then it may press on the sole at the heels. Leaving a shoe on for too long will have the same result. Pressure on the sole at this spot can cause bruising of the horn, and this is called a corn. Indeed the area of the sole between where the hoof wall and the frog meet at the heel is often called the seat of corn. Like all bruising, a corn is very painful. In this case the pain stems from the fact that the bruising causes blood and serum to escape from the sensitive tissues underneath the sole. When the top layer of horn is cut away, the bruised area can be easily identified because it is discoloured by these fluids.

Treatment of a corn first requires the cutting away of the bruised horn. You then have to ensure that no more bruising is caused, i.e. make sure that the shoes fit properly. For the first couple of shoeings it is advisable to use a special shoe (Fig. 8.4) which removes some of the pressure from the critical area of the shoe by taking it out of contact with the ground. Such a shoe can be used routinely if a horse appears to be very susceptible to corns.

Horse owners often want to improve on traditional shoeing by using studs inserted at various points around the shoe. You must realise that using any stud causes abnormal tensions in the horn of the hoof. So if you really do have to use studs, do so for as short a time as possible and remove them as soon as you can. If their use is not essential, then don't bother to fit them at all. The same applies to pads fitted between the shoe

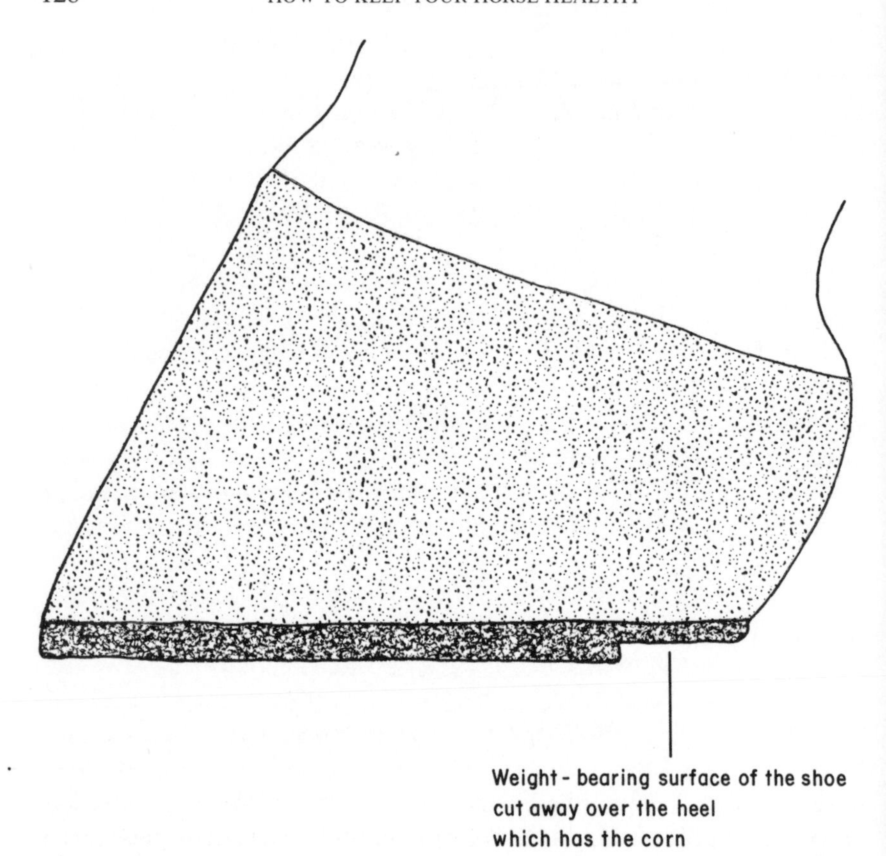

Fig. 8.4 Shoeing a horse with a corn.

and the foot. These pads are manufactured from a variety of materials, and their manufacturers claim that they reduce concussion on the foot as a whole. In fact recent investigations show that they may increase the forces on the sole and can markedly affect the balance of the foot. So once again, think long and hard before you allow yourself to be persuaded to fit such 'aids'.

The internal anatomy of the horse's foot

So far I have been considering the horse's foot, or perhaps more precisely its hoof, from the outside. Many of the problems which affect the foot do so, however, because they involve the internal structures. To simplify the anatomy of the foot, we can consider that it consists of four parts; the

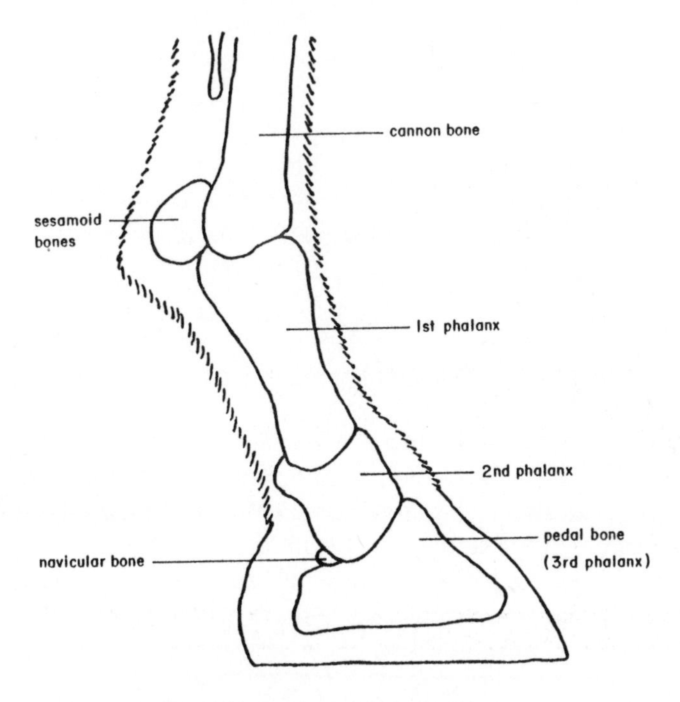

Fig. 8.5 The bones of the lower leg.

hoof, the blood supply, the bones (Fig. 8.5) and the nerve supply. The horn of the hoof consists in turn of two elements. The horn which forms the hoof wall is manufactured around the coronet and is gradually pushed downwards by new horn formed behind it until it is worn away by friction with the ground. The horn of the sole is laid down over the whole of the sole area. It is only about ½ in. (12 mm) thick, and so is replaced more rapidly than the wall. It is the horn of the hoof wall that is shod and which bears most of the weight. The hoof wall and the sole 'join' around the white line.

Although the outside of the hoof is smooth, the inside surface is anything but smooth. It is formed into thousands of small finger-like projections on the surface of the pedal bone. These are the so-called laminae. They are usually referred to as the sensitive laminae because between the horn and the bone is a very fine network of tiny blood vessels or capillaries. It is these which are associated with the pain found in so many foot conditions. Pain arises when the capillaries are stretched because the blood passing along them cannot do so quickly enough, and 'pools' in the foot. In addition to this network of capillaries there is a distinct circle of blood vessels around the coronet and the usual blood supply into the core of the bones of the foot.

We might consider there to be three bones within the hoof or foot. There is the pedal bone itself, almost hoof-shaped but much smaller. There is also the bottom end of the first of two bones which constitute the pastern. The joint between this bone, the second phalanx, and the pedal bone, or third phalanx, is below the level of the top of the hoof. Behind these two bones, and forming a joint with both of them, is the navicular bone.

The increasing problem of laminitis

Laminitis is a particularly interesting condition which affects a horse's feet as a result of something happening a considerable distance away in its stomach. It is an all too common problem of ponies especially, and many owners have to be continually on the look out to prevent the condition, especially during the grazing season. What seems to happen is that the horse or pony eats too much carbohydrate and as a result of changes in the stomach wall histamine and other substances are released into the general circulation. Having said this there are some ponies which are so susceptible to laminitis that even short periods of grazing on poor pasture can produce the effect. We still have much to learn about what makes a pony particularly susceptible to laminitis but research into this does start to look hopeful.

The foot changes in laminitis are, then, secondary to problems elsewhere. They are none the less painful for that though. We now know that the blood which comes to an affected foot down the two digital arteries does not, to a large extent, go to the foot at all. Instead it shunts, or bypasses, around the ring of coronary blood vessels and goes back up the digital veins. So far from being increased, the blood supply to the foot is reduced or slowed down during laminitis. Some blood pools in the capillaries because it either can't escape or isn't being pushed on by new blood. As the capillaries become swollen, they become painful. The heat we often feel in a foot with laminitis is not due to an increased blood flow. On the contrary, the quicker blood flows through the hoof the less chance it has to warm up the foot.

If changes in the circulation of the foot were the only problem associated with laminitis, it would not be such a serious condition. Unfortunately when the blood pools in the foot the tissues of the sensitive laminae can die because they are no longer receiving an adequate oxygen supply. This allows the pedal bone to separate from the horn which is

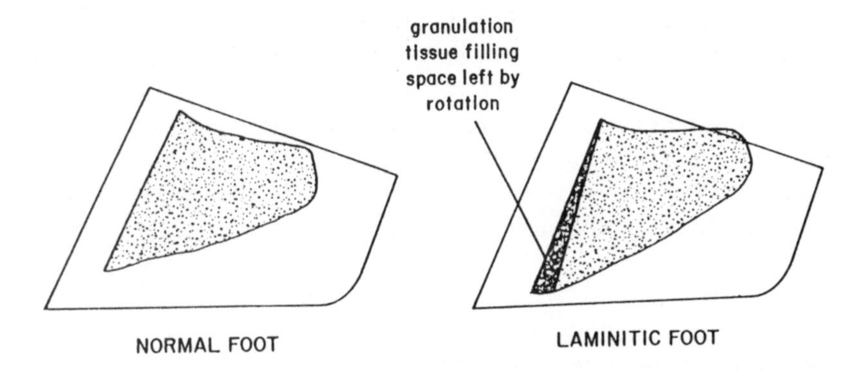

Fig. 8.6 Rotation of the pedal bone in horse with laminitis.

wrapped around it. The gap between the bone and horn soon fills with granulation tissue, which is the body's general purpose healing reaction. Unlike the situation in the healthy foot, the horn and the pedal bone are no longer anchored together firmly, with the result that every time the horse puts its foot to the ground more of the percussion forces are absorbed in this 'unstable' foot (which is painful) rather than being transmitted up the leg by a rigid structure. The other problem is that, deprived of some of its support, the pedal bone can tilt as a result of laminitis (Fig. 8.6) known as 'foundering' in the USA. The pointed toe part of the bone is then being pressed down on the sole, rather like a wedge. Indeed the bone may penetrate right through the sole.

The key to avoiding these secondary effects of laminitis lies in proper foot care. Laminitis so often occurs in horses which do not have properly balanced feet, and we assume that the imbalanced foot has disrupted circulation even more than the central cause of laminitis would have done on its own. So when a horse does develop laminitis, its feet must be trimmed back to a proper shape, even if past neglect means that this will require considerable amounts of trimming. If there is any suspicion that the pedal bone has rotated, then the feet must be X-rayed. If rotation has occurred then the horse will need to be shod in such a way as to restore the pedal bone to its normal situation parallel to the ground. In severe cases this may require drastic cutting away, or resection, of the hoof wall at the front of the foot, in order to get the front edge of the pedal bone parallel to the front edge of the hoof (Fig. 8.7). If this exposes the softer granulation tissue, then the hoof will need special dressings to prevent the establishment of infections.

It used to be thought that a healthy frog was vital to the foot because it pressed on a plexus of blood vessels as the foot bore weight, and

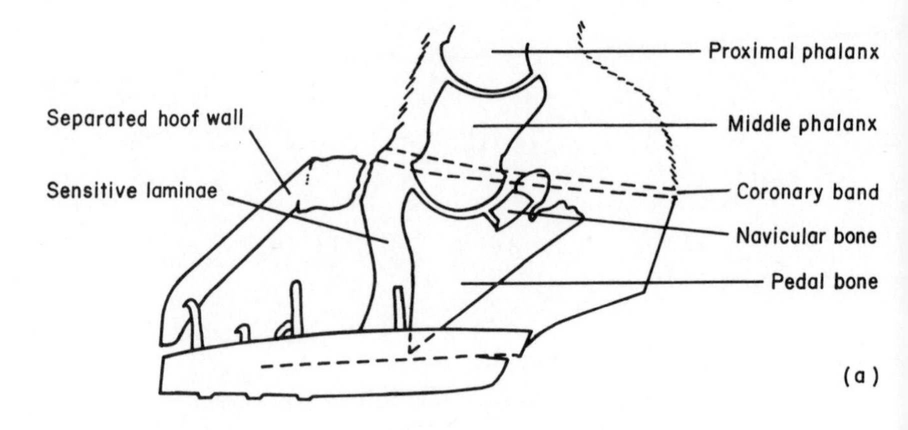

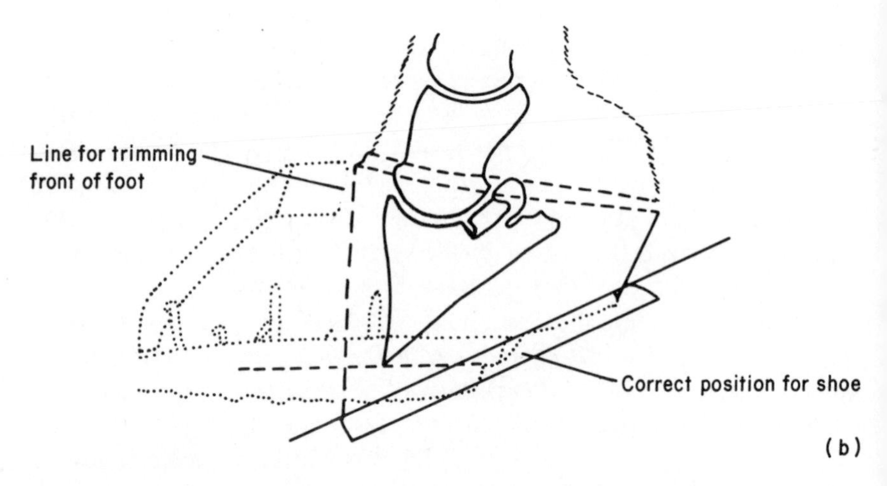

Fig. 8.7 The importance of farriery in treating laminitis. (a) Cross-section of a laminitic foot with rotation of pedal bone; (b) how foot is trimmed and then shod.

pumped blood around the foot. That is not the case: there are no significant blood vessels under the frog. We do still need a healthy, weight-bearing frog though because its fibrous pad supports the pedal bone, which supports the rest of the leg. This support is even more vital in laminitis when, as I have explained, support around the wall of the pedal bone may be lost. So a special shoe, called a heart bar shoe, may be used to provide horses with laminitis with increased frog support (Fig. 8.8).

Treatment of laminitis must also have as its primary aim the removal

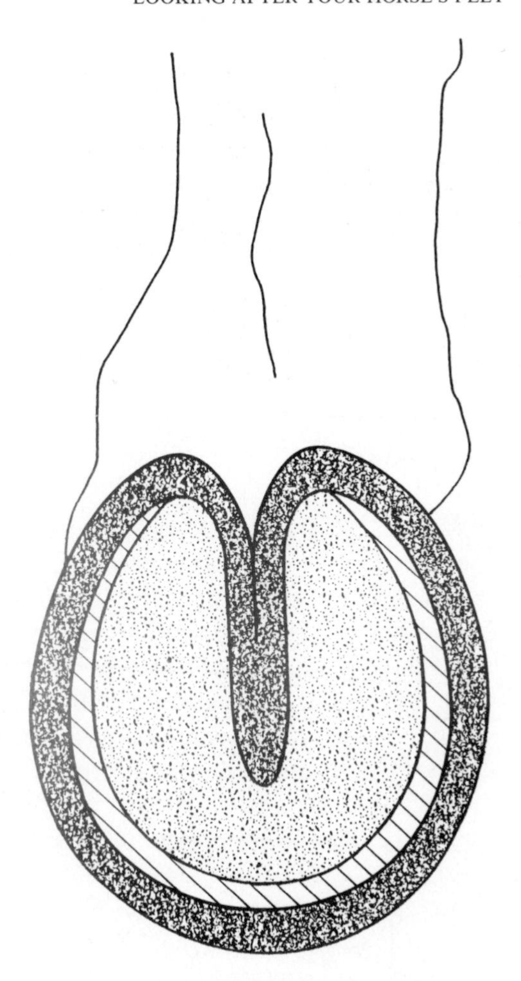

Fig. 8.8 A heart bar shoe.

of the cause of the condition, whether it be overfeeding, lack of exercise, disease (toxic laminitis may occur after a number of diseases) or whatever. There is no point in just removing the pain by the use of painkillers but leaving the cause. In the case of some ponies which develop laminitis when they are turned out to grass, this may mean that they cannot be allowed to graze at all, miserable though this may make both the pony and its owner. It is certainly true that some ponies have a predisposition to develop laminitis, and will do so in circumstances where other ponies would have no problems at all. We have much to learn as to why this happens, but there is some evidence starting to appear that there are changes in the general metabolism of these susceptible ponies.

When it comes to the use of drugs to treat laminitis, in the past this has always involved the use of anti-inflammatory drugs such as phenylbutazone and flunixen to reduce the inflammatory changes and remove the pain. This is obviously important because if we can remove the pain, the horse will be more willing to walk and exercise. If the horse moves around, this will help to stimulate the circulation in its feet. We are now also starting to use drugs which specifically affect the blood vessels of the horse's extremities. Such drugs can be very effective at increasing the blood flow (and so reducing the painful pooling of blood) in the horse's feet.

Navicular disease and its control

Common though laminitis is as a cause of lameness in ponies, the commonest cause of chronic foot lameness in horses is almost certainly navicular disease. This is a problem which classically affects horses at the peak of their active life. So horses often first show symptoms at eight to ten years of age, although we tend to push our competition horses harder than we used to do, so they may show symptoms earlier. It is relatively less common in racehorses than other types because they have such a short athletic life. Nevertheless it is Thoroughbreds and Thoroughbred crosses which seem most commonly affected overall. There is another feature of navicular disease which has a distinct bearing on whether a particular horse will get navicular disease or not, and that is that horses often start to show symptoms about six weeks after a change in routine. So they often develop the disease a month or two after purchase, or after a change of stableyard. It is important that anyone thinking of buying a horse appreciates this tendency. You can spend a great deal of time choosing a horse which you or your veterinary advisor thinks does not have navicular disease, only to find that it still develops symptoms soon afterwards. It is not the fault of the person who sold the horse, and anyway if the horse was already obviously suffering from the disease the symptoms would have shown within a week or so of purchase as the effects of any masking drugs wore off. This time of peak incidence of navicular disease is probably due to a combination of several factors including the tendency for owners to work their new horse hard because of their initial enthusiasm, and also the fact that a different farrier and shoeing interval may be involved.

Navicular disease causes a chronic lameness of one or both front feet. The lameness may wear off during the course of exercise, especially in the early stages. After a short period (even as little as 30 minutes) of rest the lameness returns, however. With rest the symptoms may improve, only to reappear when the horse is returned to regular work. There are no detectable reasons for the lameness from the owner's point of view; no heat, swelling or site of pain. Indeed this absence of any symptoms other than lameness often sows the first seeds of suspicion that it might be navicular disease.

Nobody can diagnose navicular disease merely by looking at the horse, however strong the circumstantial evidence may be. There are two requirements which have to be met before a definite diagnosis can be made. First of all it must be proved that the lameness is due to a problem within the foot, and not elsewhere. This is done by injecting local anaesthetic around the nerve on either side of the leg which leads to the foot. This prevents the horse feeling any pain in the foot. Such a nerve block, as it is called, is said to be positive if the horse trots sound afterwards, but was lame beforehand. Because navicular disease so often affects both front feet, carrying out a nerve block on one foot may still leave the horse lame but a skilled observer will notice that it is then lame on the other leg, i.e. both of a horse's front feet may hurt but it will appear to be lame on the one which hurts the most.

The second part of the confirmation that a horse has navicular disease consists of finding changes indicative of the disease on X-ray pictures of one or more feet. To appreciate what those changes might be it is first necessary to know what navicular disease really is. Modern thinking is that there are a number of different changes which can occur in the foot and cause the set of symptoms which we call navicular disease. These changes may each have slightly different causes, but they all involve the part of foot around the navicular bone (Fig. 8.5). Originally it was suggested that the pain came from a 'wear and tear' arthritis, involving the navicular bone. Then it was suggested it was associated with areas of dying bone within the navicular bone. Present thinking is that the pain is the result of increased pressure within the blood vessels to and from the area, and that the changes we see are therefore secondary to the lameness. One advantage of the latter theory is that it explains why we can get a variety of changes all producing the same 'disease'.

The navicular bone itself is one of a number of bones down the leg which are not an essential part of the skeleton itself but which act as a fulcrum to change the direction or tension of a muscle/tendon system. In this case it is the deep flexor tendon, which runs around the back of the navicular bone before at last attaching on to the pedal bone. When we get changes to the blood supply to the navicular bone, we get bone dying or altering in its density. These changes can be seen on an X-ray. The precise interpretation of the X-ray changes which may indicate navicular disease is a matter for the veterinary surgeon involved with a particular case rather than for a book such as this. The borderline between normal and abnormal can be very blurred, and diagnosis can never be made on X-ray grounds alone. A sound horse with X-ray changes has not got navicular disease (although there is an increased likelihood of it occurring in the future). It is, however, possible to have a lame horse which does not yet show any X-ray visible changes. Similarly the amount of change seen on an X-ray does not indicate the severity of the problem. There are horses which are permanently and severely lame but which have less X-ray changes than another horse which is only occasionally lame. So X-rays can confirm a diagnosis of navicular disease but they have limitations and cannot be used as the sole basis for the initial diagnosis. Apart from the generalisation that if X-ray changes are present as well as lameness then the horse has probably had symptoms of some sort for about four to six weeks, it is not possible to 'age' how long a horse has had navicular disease.

If you are unfortunate enough to own a horse which becomes lame as a result of navicular disease, what should you do? The first thing is to have the horse's feet properly balanced as I have described. There are varying opinions as to the best kind of shoe which should be used. In some countries a shoe with a bar across the heels is commonly used. In the UK greater emphasis is placed on using a shoe with a rolled toe and attaching

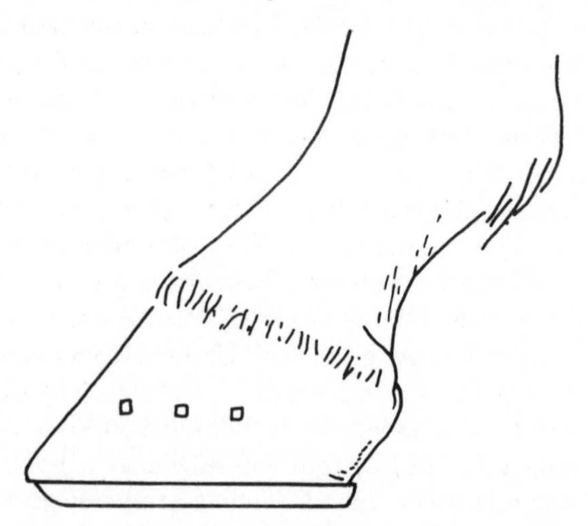

Fig. 8.9 Lateral view of a foot shod for navicular disease. Notice how the rolled toe is set very slightly back from the toe of the hoof, whilst the heels of the shoe similarly extend fractionally back behind the hoof.

it slightly further back than is normal (Fig. 8.9). This ensures good support and protection for the heel of the foot, which is, of course, the site of navicular disease. Shoeing may need to be carried out more frequently than usual, because as the hoof grows not only will it become unbalanced but the shoe will no longer extend that vital fraction behind the hoof at the heels.

From the horse's welfare point of view, steps should obviously be taken to relieve the pain associated with navicular disease. The commonest drug used for this is phenylbutazone ('bute'). This is effective in the majority of cases, is relatively inexpensive, and will enable most horses with navicular disease to return to normal work. Unfortunately anti-inflammatory drugs such as phenylbutazone do not cure navicular disease. If given on a permanent basis, they may enable the horse to lead a normal life, but that does not make the horse itself normal. Navicular disease tends to be a progressive disease, that is to say it gets worse with continuing wear and tear. So although a horse with navicular disease may hunt successfully for several years on phenylbutazone, the very activity which the drugs makes possible will be aggravating the problem until eventually the condition becomes so painful that the horse is lame even on regular medication. Another disadvantage of the permanent use of such painkillers is that many of the official bodies which control competitions such as horse trials, racing, etc. either do not allow competitors to use any drugs at all, or only allow phenylbutazone at such a low dose that it is unlikely to be effective as a painkiller.

For centuries navicular disease has been considered an incurable disease. As such the only treatment was to remove the pain either by cutting the nerves which supply the foot or, more recently, by using painkillers. A permanent cure is now possible for some (but not all) cases. This involves the use of drugs which restore the 'proper' blood flow to the region. This removes the pain and some of the physical changes, although the bony changes which we see on X-rays are rather like scars, and will still be detectable. On the other hand they will not get any worse, as would otherwise be the case. The first of these drugs which was used was warfarin, better known as a rat poison. Great care has to be taken in its use because if too much is given, it will stop the horse's blood clotting just as it does that of the rat, and the horse will be at the risk of dying from a fatal haemorrhage. So throughout the time that a horse is receiving warfarin, it will need to be blood-sampled every six weeks (and more frequently at times) to check that its clotting mechanism is not disturbed too much. Another drug which restores blood flow to the foot is isoxsuprine. This is a safer drug and treatment can be increased or decreased without any need for blood sampling. Although according to some statistics, it may not be quite as likely to effect a cure as warfarin, it does hold out more chance of the horse returning to competitions. This is because treatment is normally completed within three to six months, and once the horse is no longer receiving the drug it can compete again without any risk of failing a dope test. Treatment with warfarin is usually continued for at least one or two years because of the difficulties in starting up the treatment again if more treatment proves necessary.

Avoiding navicular disease

As I have already indicated, many horse owners have their first experience of navicular disease with a 'new' horse. For this reason they want to know how best to avoid buying a susceptible horse. First of all beware of a horse which has been competing regularly but has then been rested before its sale. Jumping, for instance, tends to aggravate navicular disease because of the percussion involved, and so affected horses may lose their form or even become lame only to go sound with rest. When you go to look at a horse there are two simple things to do. First of all, always give the horse 20–30 minutes' rest after you have ridden it, and then trot it out to check for lameness. With navicular disease an apparently sound horse may well be slightly lame at this stage, although by the next day (or even sooner) it is sound again. Secondly, try holding up a front leg with the foot bent backwards at the fetlock as hard as you can for 30 seconds, and then trot the horse straight away. Holding the foot in this way increases the pressure in the blood vessels, and so increases the amount of lameness seen. Although this test is not completely specific for navicular disease, normal horses never go lame when you do it. So if it makes a potential purchase go lame on one or both front legs, avoid the horse at all costs.

One vexed question is whether one should have a horse's feet X-rayed before deciding whether to buy it or not. On balance I would suggest that these X-rays may be more of a hindrance than a help. Even if they show nothing, the horse may still be lame due to navicular disease within two or three months of purchase. If the horse has widespread changes in the navicular bone, a proper veterinary examination will certainly detect some abnormality or lameness. If, more awkwardly, only slight X-ray changes are detected, then you are left in a no man's land. It is impossible to say whether these changes will ever progress and cause lameness or not. We must remember that lameness is the final arbitrator as to whether a horse has navicular disease or not, not X-ray changes. If you turn such a horse down, you may lose the opportunity to buy a sound horse which never goes lame. On the other hand, if you buy it you may get very little use from it before it goes lame again. So in many ways you are no better off than if you had not gone to the expense of having the X-rays taken.

Of course there are many foot problems which it is impossible to foresee or prevent. You can never tell when a horse will tread on a sharp flint or nail and introduce infection which develops into an abscess. In this book, however, I am concentrating on what you can do to keep your horse healthy by preventing disease.

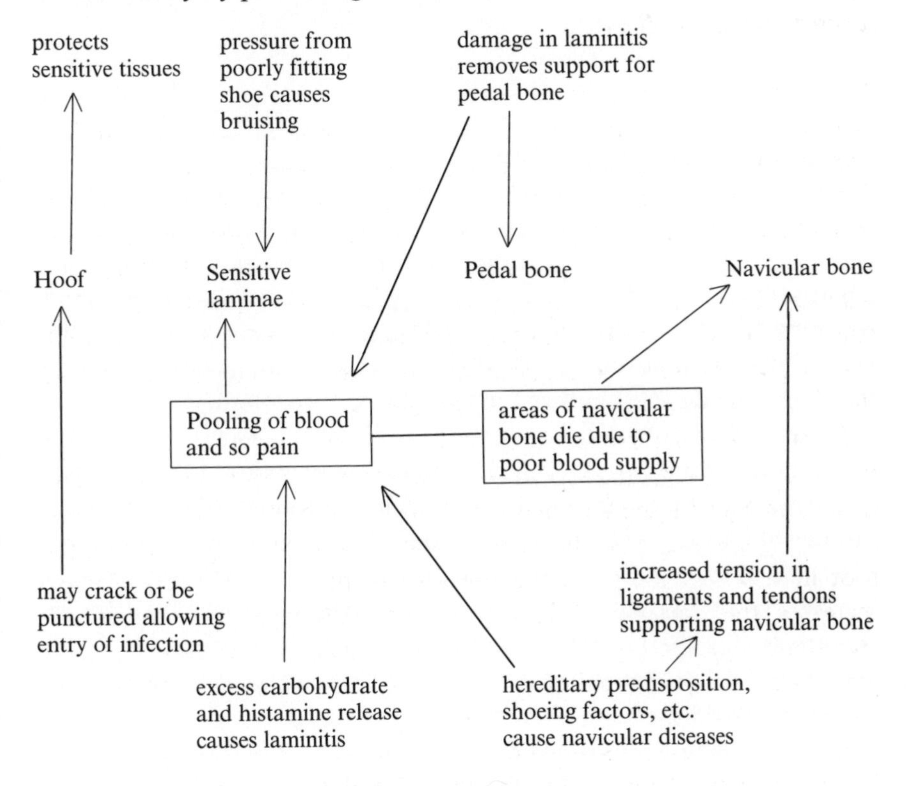

Fig. 8.10 Foot lameness.

9 Mental health

It can sometimes be difficult to define precisely what we mean by health. If a horse has colic it has something demonstrably wrong with it and so is not healthy. If a horse has ringworm then it is equally obviously not healthy. Over the centuries, several situations have been recognised where the horse appears healthy but habitually performs some action which is very abnormal (and usually detrimental to its overall welfare). These habits are called vices rather than diseases. Because they may have a detrimental effect on the horse and because these undesirable behavioural patterns are all too readily copied by other horses in the yard, recognised stable vices have come to occupy a middle position between definite disease and normal behaviour. As a result, a purchaser of a horse which proves to have a stable vice that was not declared at the time of sale can almost invariably return the horse and obtain a refund of his or her money. Because a horse with such a vice has nothing physically wrong which can be detected during a clinical examination, vices are specifically excluded from the scope of the examination carried out by a veterinary surgeon at the time of purchase.

Although this book is mainly about the maintenance of the horse's physical health, there is no doubt that mental and psychological aspects of management have a considerable role in keeping a horse healthy. There has been little formal work on this topic, but years of experience have shown that, like other creatures, including we humans, horses do thrive and do better, including work better, when mentally content.

The horse is an amazingly adaptable animal. It moulds itself well to our work requirements and the management systems we impose upon it provided it can do so within its individual capabilities. And all horses are very much individuals, of course. One can give general rules and guidelines but owners and managers are responsible for deciding when they need to be adapted to suit the individuals in their care.

Stabling of any sort, whether in loose boxes/box stalls or standing/tie stalls, is a very artificial way of keeping a horse, but horses obviously do take to it well *if* they receive ample exercise (normally at least two hours daily for a healthy horse fit for moderate to hard work), if they can be with other horses (but not near those with which they do not get on) and preferably have some natural social contact with them, if possible at liberty, and if they are fed and otherwise managed according to their physical requirements.

Some individuals, however, do *not* take well to our artificial management methods and when this is detected steps should be taken to make allowances for them and implement changes in their management to ensure as far as possible that they are more content. If horses are overstressed mentally, worried by their environment, it is likely that physical disorders will result, as in humans. Any overstress, mental or physical, puts an unnecessary overload on the horse's systems which results in the body's resources going to try to combat that stress. This means that those resources are reduced when called upon for such things as fighting off disease or healing injuries. Physical strength may also be reduced and the horse's entire physical performance can be detrimentally affected.

Stable vices

There are two factors which are usually common to stable vices. Firstly, the horse often starts to behave like this as a result of boredom, but vices and other undesirable behaviour patterns may be largely neurotic reactions to inappropriate management methods for the individual involved, and it is noticeable that horses kept in a fairly natural environment (by domesticated standards) do not usually exhibit them unless they have been previously confirmed in them when under different management methods. Vices such as box-walking, weaving, crib-biting (cribbing) and wind-sucking are not seen in wild or feral equidae to the best of my knowledge.

By making a horse's stable routine as interesting as possible whilst sticking to a regular timetable of feeding, you may prevent your horse developing a vice. Exercise and having interesting things to see when it puts its head out of the stable door help prevent boredom. It follows, therefore, that the top stable door should be left open whenever possible.

The other common factor is that vices often (but not always) appear to be 'infectious' in that if one horse in a yards develops a vice then the other horses which can see the afflicted horse tend to copy its behaviour.

As anyone who has had the care of an afflicted horse will know, it is usually impossible to stop the horse performing its vice. Various physical methods such as cribbing straps, bales of straw scattered around the box and two bricks suspended in the stable doorway have been tried with a view to 'correcting', respectively, crib-biting, box-walking and weaving, but with little success because apart from the fact that the vices recur with full force the moment these physical restraints are removed, they do not, of course, stop the horse wanting to perform its vice – or needing to.

And 'need' is probably a more appropriate word than 'want' in this case, because, as research work in Holland and the USA is showing, many, maybe even all, animals exhibiting any kind of vice which involves repeated physical activity, such as the four just mentioned, are 'natural junkies', for want of a better expression. There is evidence to suggest that the repeated routine movements involved may lead to the release of higher levels of endorphins, natural morphine-like chemicals. These act as the body's own pain killers and also induce a feeling of euphoria similar to that experienced by a drug addict, who may be addicted to a drug of the same family, which includes heroin and opium.

Horses who may begin a vice as a nervous release from the tension of, say, being stabled, deprived of close equine company such as would be experienced during turning out, being corn-fed and worked hard, or whatever, produce these endorphins which give some relief from the tension and stress in their lives, so giving themselves a natural 'fix'. Once started, the fix becomes a necessity quite quickly and the horse becomes addicted to its own body's drugs. As experienced horsemasters will know, it is sometimes possible to stop a vice in the very early stages provided the management is also altered to relieve the over-stress the horse is feeling, but once a vice becomes confirmed (i.e. the horse becomes addicted) it is more or less impossible to stop its performance without the use of physical restraints, as mentioned. As discussed, these restraints are not really the answer, not least because they are simply making matters worse by removing the horse's release from tension. Most horses, prevented from performing a specific vice, will simply find something else to do instead and become the victims of two or more vices.

Horses have been kept free of a long-established vice for several days by putting them on continual intravenous drip of an anti-morphine drug. Unfortunately, within hours of the drug being withdrawn, the horses were exhibiting the vice again just as strongly.

It may well be, therefore, that stable vices are the horse's way of doping itself to relieve boredom and frustration. That does not explain, of course, how the first affected horse 'pushes' the idea to its stable companions and persuades them to try it. Like all morphine problems, vices are addictive, and once a horse develops a vice it will usually always exhibit it. One notable exception to this is that when a horse changes stables and/or owners then, perhaps as a result of a feeling of insecurity in the new pecking order, it may indulge in one of these vices for a few days. This is similar to a smoker who smokes more heavily when under stress. The vice may well disappear again as the horse gains confidence. So if a newly purchased horse shows evidence of a recognised stable vice you should advise the old owner promptly, in case you require them to take the horse back. You should not, however, be surprised if the problem disappears before you have a chance to return the horse.

Weaving

Perhaps the easiest vice to notice is when a horse weaves. Such a horse stands with its head over the door, swaying from side to side for minutes or even hours on end. As it sways, its weight shifts from one fore leg to the other and back again. The way to prevent a horse weaving is, as I have indicated, to make its life more interesting. This means that although other horses may copy it unless it is stopped, you should not move the horse to an isolated stable away from the general stable yard activity. Nor should you close the top stable door. Apart from anything else, horses can still weave as they stand in a corner of the stable. Fitting a half-grille to the stable door with a U-shaped space to allow the horse to look out but not to weave usually solves the problem. Alternatively hang two small heavy logs in the doorway half a yard/metre apart so that if the horse weaves it will knock against the logs.

When is a crib-biter a windsucker?

There is some confusion as to where the dividing line lies between the vices of windsucking and crib-biting. In order to clarify the situation, the British Equine Veterinary Association has defined the two vices as follows:

Crib-biting is a vice of domesticated horses and pones which consists of the habitual grasping of fixed objects with the incisor teeth. It may be associated with windsucking. Windsucking is a vice of domesticated horses and ponies which consists of the habitual swallowing of air. So it is possible for a horse to crib-bite although it does not swallow any air. Similarly some horses can swallow air without needing to fix their jaws on a solid object first.

Crib-biting is undesirable on two particular counts. It wears away the front edges of the horse's incisor teeth, thus drastically affecting our ability to age the horse accurately by its dentition. Crib-biting can also be very expensive for the stable owner because of the damage caused to the wooden parts of the stable. Occasionally horses which crib-bite and windsuck in the field loosen fencing posts so much that it is impossible to keep the horse safely fenced in. The owner may even have to contemplate euthanasia if they cannot afford to stable the horse throughout the year. Windsucking may interfere with a horse's digestion because it fills the stomach with air rather than food. As a result the horse may be more prone to colic or it may lose bodily condition.

Crib-biting can usually be controlled by removing from the stable any objects such as mangers which the horse might fix its jaws on, and feeding the horse on the floor. There are proprietary substances which can be thickly coated on the remaining edges to deter the vice. To be effective such substances must be applied generously, which is both messy and expensive. In order to windsuck, the horse needs to move its larynx. A special rigid strap can be fixed around the horse's neck to prevent this movement. To be effective, the strap must be applied quite firmly, although obviously loose enough to allow normal breathing. Various surgical techniques have also been developed to prevent the problem. The most acceptable of these involves removing short lengths of the muscles and nerve along the lower neck which fix and move the larynx.

The learning process

When dealing with any mental problem in the horse, we have to remember that the horse learns quickly. It is not a moral being, however, and so it does not differentiate between good and bad lessons. It will learn both just as quickly. We expect the horse to respond quickly and permanently to our training under saddle, so we must not be surprised if it responds quickly and permanently to a bad habit such as kicking the stable door or escaping from the field or stable.

If there is some minor procedure we have to carry out which we expect to be unpleasant to the horse, we should first of all habituate the horse by repeatedly carrying out the non-painful part of the procedure, e.g. patting the horse's neck firmly prior to actually inserting the needle for an intramuscular injection. As you do this you will notice that there comes a point where the horse ceases to look at you and starts to ignore what you are doing. If you then complete the procedure, the horse will usually not object at all. As a guide, a survey found that on average you needed to repeat an action 16 times before the horse becomes acclimatised. Incidentally, there is a firm division down the centre of a horse's brain. Even though a horse has come to accept you carrying out a procedure on one side, it may well need to be habituated all over again before it allows you to carry out the procedure on the other side.

When a horse really does play up and prevents you attending to minor injuries, it is usually better to apply a twitch in an attempt to restrain it rather than allow the horse to 'learn' that when it misbehaves it gets its own way. A traditional twitch consists of a loop of rope fastened to the end of a length of wood. The loop is placed round a large fold of the horse's upper lip, and the handle is twisted until it tightens the loop so much that it will not pull off. Amazingly the horse will often then allow you to carry out procedures which would have provoked rearing or kicking without the twitch. Although the effect of the twitch has been known for a very long time, it is only recently that we have discovered why it works. It appears that while the twitch is applied to the horse's upper lip it stimulates the release into the horse's bloodstream of endorphins. These act as painkillers throughout the system, enabling you to deal with wounds etc. anywhere on the horse's body. They also have some sedative effect, quietening the horse down. The twitch which I have described has now been considerably improved by the manufacture of a humane horse restrainer. This used a hinged pair of specially shaped pieces of smooth metal to grip the lip. This is quicker to apply, fits any size of horse and does not mark the skin of the lip at all. Perhaps because of these factors, these humane restrainers appear to be more effective than a rope twitch.

Head shaking

Before leaving the question of behavioural problems and vices, there is one disease which deserves a mention. Actually it is not a specific disease at all, but rather a very undesirable symptom which can have many causes. It is head shaking. By this we do not mean the occasional shake of the head which all horses give from time to time. Rather the term applies to the violent movements of a horse's head (usually up and down) when it is being ridden. In severe cases the head shaking may make it impossible to ride the horse safely at all.

Over a hundred different causes of such apparently uncontrollable head shaking have been described, but there still remain a substantial number of cases every year which do not appear to have any detectable physical cause. The condition can literally appear overnight, and naturally has a disastrous effect on the horse's value. Not surprisingly people have tried all sorts of remedies to cure the condition. Most of these are connected with flies, because the problem only shows itself in the warmer, humid months and disappears completely once the frosts appear. Although fly fringes around the nose or eyes appear to prevent head shaking in some horses, it has never been possible to prove exactly what it is that the horse sees or senses and which triggers off such a violent reaction. All one can do is to offer sympathy to the frustrated owner, and encourage them to experiment with ways to stop the problem if it is possible to do so safely without the rider being literally knocked off the horse by the head movements. Modern science does not like to admit complete defeat. Even in the case of the common cold we can detect the viruses which cause the problem although we cannot yet kill them off. In the case of these head shakers of unknown origin science has drawn a complete blank. We can neither find the cause nor offer a cure.

Feeding

Feeding is another area which often leaves much to be desired on the general management front. Horses are by nature grass and, to a lesser extent, leaf eaters. Cereal grains would never, in the wild, form a large part of the horse's diet, and, in any case, only be available at one time of year, yet, because of their concentrated nature which enables us to get more nutrients inside our hard-working horses, we tend to feed them all year round whenever our horses are in work. This method of feeding does not suit all horses, and perhaps there is a case for looking at our general ideas of feeding with a view to trying to feed better quality roughage (hay or hay substitutes) and fewer concentrates, and also allowing the horses a more natural, virtually round the clock, access to that roughage.

Digestion is largely effected by micro-flora and micro-fauna in the horse's gut, as well as by chemical digestive juices. These gut organisms, being living creatures, also need a pretty constant supply of food, like the horse itself, if they are to remain healthy – indeed, alive. Erratic feeding

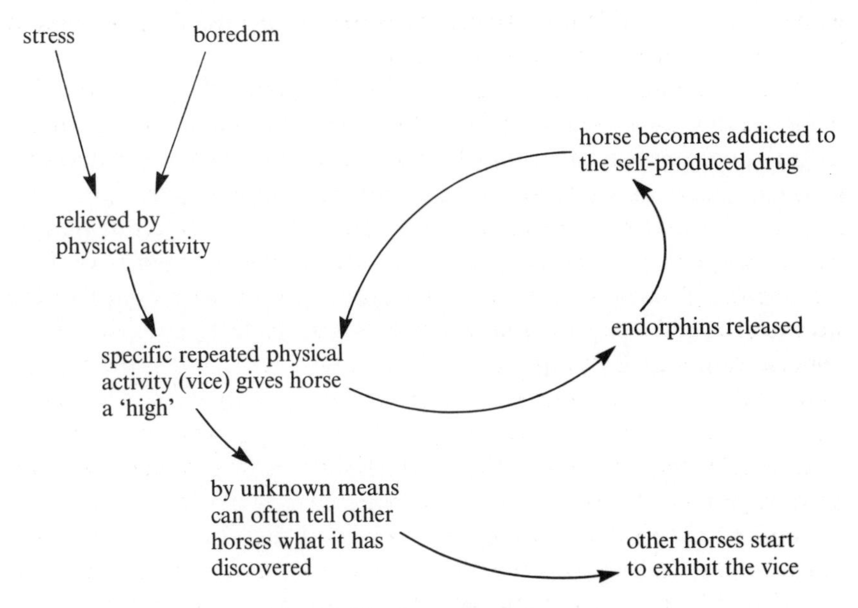

Fig. 9.1 Development of vices.

methods which leave the horse without any food for several, sometimes many, hours actively kill off these gut organisms, or seriously debilitate them, so decreasing the efficiency of the horse's digestive system and, consequently, his general health and wellbeing, so such methods are counter-productive.

'Feed little and often' is one of the so-called Golden Rules of feeding, yet very many horses are not fed this way. They receive two or three concentrate feeds per day and have hay night and morning only; they are, therefore without any food at all for an unnaturally large number of hours out of the 24 – hardly conducive to digestive health. Fewer concentrates, better quality roughage and a more constant supply would seem to be points well worth considering in the management of horses. It is also important to feed a little of *all* the dietary ingredients in *each* feed to supply the gut organisms with their own constant supply of their particular food (some being able to process one type of food and some another, and so on), rather than giving the horse, for example, grain in one feed, nuts in the next, coarse mix in the next, and so on in the belief that this provides a change for it and will help it retain an interest in its food. A horse with a healthy digestive system will be ready and willing to eat what it needs, anyway.

Basically, however, to keep horses more content mentally, the real 'secret' is to keep them more naturally, with more personal space, liberty, natural social contact with other horses (i.e. turning out together) and a more natural feeding regime. A healthy, happy mind really does help produce and maintain a healthy, fit body.

Prevention is always better than cure, and the real answer to preventing vices and generally undesirable behaviour patterns, and of promoting a mentally content state, is to manage horses in such a way as to prevent their wanting or needing to react to over-stress. More natural management and, according to the individual, a lighter workload and more amenable work would be appropriate. If we keep asking The Big Question, as is the popular phrase these days, there will come a day when the horse can't or won't answer it.

whether they could be done on the same day. Remember that it will probably cost you more to have the veterinary surgeon come to the stable than for the actual vaccination, so a saved visit will more than pay for giving the vaccination early. Remember also that at present in the UK you may choose to vaccinate against equine influenza, tetanus or EHV1 virus. It may or may not be appropriate to vaccinate against each disease at very different times during the year. If you are vaccinating against EHV1 to prevent abortion, for instance, you will probably be doing so at a different time of the year than if you were trying to prevent respiratory disease.

The next step is to decide how frequently you are going to have your horse shod, and, in conjunction with your farrier mark those weeks on the planner. Remember that any period over six weeks will result in you riding a horse with improperly balanced feet. If for any reason a shoeing has to be delayed, do not alter the next date. If you do, you will tend to find at the end of the year that your horse has only been shod four or five times rather than six or seven. The difference might not seem much, but the extra stresses and strains on the feet may be significant. The third step is to plan your worming programme. The advice given in Chapter 6 will help you do this, and your veterinary surgeon will be only too happy to help you take into consideration any special factors relating to your problems or locality. Again you should be working around a basic frequency of worming every eight weeks. Whichever drug you are using routinely, you should use one which is active against bots at the worming nearest to December. It also makes sense to worm immediately before turning out to grass, in order to reduce pasture contamination, and immediately after a stabling period begins, in order to remove worms picked up at pasture. If your horse has to go away while you are on holiday because there is no-one to look after it, then you should plan to worm it on its return with a drug which is effective against worm larvae.

Pregnant mares obviously pose slightly different problems. The whole system will revolve around the expected foaling months. Please note that I use the word 'months' rather than 'days'. A mare can give birth to a perfectly normal, full-term foal up to a month before or a month after the 340th day, which is considered the 'normal' foaling date. Ideally, therefore, you should complete your preparations around a month before you expect the mare to foal. If the mare is going away to stud to foal, she should do so in plenty of time, so that she has a chance to build up good antibody levels against any infections present on the stud which were not present at her home stable. There is now available a very simple test which will tell you when a mare is getting close to foaling. It merely involves adding a few drops of 'milk' from the mare's udder to a solution, and looking at the colour change that takes place on a special paper strip which is dipped into the resulting solution. A positive reaction indicates that the mare will probably foal in the next 12 hours.

Many stallion owners require swabs to have been taken from a mare before she visits the stallion, in order to ensure that she is not carrying infections such as contagious equine metritis (CEM). When you select a stallion to which to mate a mare, you should check the swabbing requirements and enter them on the year planner so that they do not get forgotten. Later on, pregnancy testing often needs to be carried out at precise times in order to confirm whether a further payment is necessary to the stallion owner. It is in the mare owner's interest to ensure that these requirements are met, otherwise he or she will be liable for the payment even if the mare is no longer pregnant.

Memory can be a chancy thing. If asked when their horse last had its teeth rasped, many owners would have difficulty in giving a definite answer. Every horse should have its teeth checked at least once a year, and this should be entered on the planner. Many owners combine this dental check with the horse's routine vaccination. This is not an ideal arrangement, because the vaccinations should be carried out whilst the horse is resting out at grass, whereas any tooth rasping should be carried out as near as possible to the time of performance and concentrate feeding.

Horses being asked to perform very precise work such as dressage may benefit from more frequent checking. They may also benefit from the routine removal of their wolf teeth. These are small teeth which appear in some horses just immediately in front of the upper molar teeth. They should not be confused with the tushes which may be situated midway between the incisor and molar teeth. Wolf teeth are anchored in the gums, not the jaw bone. So pressure from the bit can easily rock them and cause discomfort, which is reflected in reduced performance.

I have often been impressed to walk into a tack room and see a blackboard detailing exactly what each horse should be given in the way of food. Unfortunately all too often when I return weeks or months later, the same entries are still written up. Feeding schedules must be flexible, following the needs of both horse and trainer. So every time a significant change is made in the amounts you feed, i.e. if the quantity of an ingredient is altered by more than ½ lb (200 g), then write the new formula on the planner. It may also be interesting to make a note of why the formula has been changed. So if you decide that the horse is losing weight when performing a certain amount of work, then recording that fact may save you making the same mistake on a later occasion.

The final stage in preparing the master plan is to enter on it somewhere any background information you may have on your horse. So, as has been discussed earlier, its resting heart or pulse rate should be known and you can enter it here, and similarly its resting respiratory rate. If any 'healthy' blood samples have been taken, then the levels of these can be entered for comparison with any 'disease' levels which might need taking later on.

Warming up for exercise

The discipline which is needed to keep your horse's health planned and recorded on paper can also be applied to planning a 'start-up' routine every time you exercise your horse. Before you even take the horse out of the stable, flex all four legs by holding them up and fully bent for several seconds. The front legs should also be extended forwards and straight (or rather partially bent because the horse must bend the leg when it comes forward). Next run your hand down all four legs, feeling for any unusual heat or swelling.

When you bring the horse out of the stable (or field if it is not being

Table 10.1 The overall planner checklist.

Tick that you have marked the following on the plan	✓
Holidays for you	
Periods horse turned out (if appropriate)	
Dates vaccinations due	
Shoeing dates	
Worming dates	
Foaling date etc.	
Feeding formulae	
Resting heart and respiratory rates	
Any routine healthy blood values known	

stabled), then you should get into the routine of trotting the horse away and back for 20–30 years/metres in hand. If you are entirely on your own, then this will only serve to further loosen up the muscles of movement. If you have another person with you, however, then they should be able to tell you whether your horse's head nods or its backside sinks down as it trots along. Once you climb into the saddle, you lose the opportunity to detect mild lameness. It doesn't matter if the observer isn't an expert. They do not have to be able to tell you on which leg the horse is lame. It is sufficient to know that you have a problem, so that you can take the necessary steps to deal with it. When you have gone through this procedure, you can mount with confidence that all is well.

Even if you follow all these measures, you must not sit back complacently. Keeping your horse healthy requires constant attention to detail. I hope this book will have helped to guide your attention.

Index